INTERNET THEORY, TECHNOLOGY AND APPLICATIONS

RURAL BROADBAND

SELECTED ANALYSES OF DEPLOYMENT AND LOAN PROGRAMS

INTERNET THEORY, TECHNOLOGY AND APPLICATIONS

INTERNET THEORY, TECHNOLOGY AND APPLICATIONS

RURAL BROADBAND

SELECTED ANALYSES OF DEPLOYMENT AND LOAN PROGRAMS

CLYDE L. HORN
EDITOR

publishers
New York

For permission to use material from this book please contact us:
Telephone 631-231-7269; Fax 631-231-8175
Web Site: http://www.novapublishers.com

NOTICE TO THE READER

The Publisher has taken reasonable care in the preparation of this book, but makes no expressed or implied warranty of any kind and assumes no responsibility for any errors or omissions. No liability is assumed for incidental or consequential damages in connection with or arising out of information contained in this book. The Publisher shall not be liable for any special, consequential, or exemplary damages resulting, in whole or in part, from the readers' use of, or reliance upon, this material. Any parts of this book based on government reports are so indicated and copyright is claimed for those parts to the extent applicable to compilations of such works.

Independent verification should be sought for any data, advice or recommendations contained in this book. In addition, no responsibility is assumed by the publisher for any injury and/or damage to persons or property arising from any methods, products, instructions, ideas or otherwise contained in this publication.

This publication is designed to provide accurate and authoritative information with regard to the subject matter covered herein. It is sold with the clear understanding that the Publisher is not engaged in rendering legal or any other professional services. If legal or any other expert assistance is required, the services of a competent person should be sought. FROM A DECLARATION OF PARTICIPANTS JOINTLY ADOPTED BY A COMMITTEE OF THE AMERICAN BAR ASSOCIATION AND A COMMITTEE OF PUBLISHERS.

Additional color graphics may be available in the e-book version of this book.

Library of Congress Cataloging-in-Publication Data

ISBN: 978-1-63463-215-7

Published by Nova Science Publishers, Inc. † New York

CONTENTS

PREFACE

This book addresses how RUS ensures that projects are completed by the deadline and as approved and the extent to which RUS provides information to show BIP's impact. It also discusses the progress of broadband projects, their effect on expanding access to and adoption of broadband, and any challenges awardees face in completing projects and agency actions to address these challenges.

Chapter 1 – Access to affordable broadband is seen as vital to economic growth and improved quality of life, yet its deployment in rural areas can be costly. The American Recovery and Reinvestment Act of 2009 (Recovery Act) appropriated funding for BIP, a USDA RUS program to fund broadband projects to provide service to end users in mostly rural areas. By 2010, RUS had awarded over $3 billion, primarily to 297 infrastructure projects, and required that projects be completed by June 2015 in approved areas.

GAO was asked to review BIP's results and impact. This report addresses (1) how RUS ensures that projects are completed by the deadline and as approved and (2) the extent to which RUS provides information to show BIP's impact. GAO interviewed RUS officials, reviewed policies, and analyzed RUS project data as of March 2014. GAO also interviewed five awardees from a nongeneralizable sample of seven BIP projects selected in part based on award size and location.

Chapter 2 – Access to affordable broadband telecommunications is increasingly viewed as vital to economic growth and improved quality of life. Broadband is particularly critical in rural areas, where advanced communications can reduce the isolation of remote communities and individuals. To extend access to broadband and therefore increase economic opportunity in rural America, RUS finances the construction of broadband through a loan program.

GAO was asked to assess issues related to the loan program. This report addresses the (1) geographic distribution and financial performance of loans and (2) relationship between loans and broadband deployment and economic development, and how USDA evaluates progress towards these outcomes.

To address these research questions, GAO interviewed broadband providers and stakeholders selected for their varying experiences, including those that have and have not received RUS loans. GAO also analyzed RUS and U.S. Census Bureau data from 2003— 2013 as well as the most recent National Broadband Map data.

Chapter 3 – Access to affordable broadband service is seen as vital to economic growth and improved quality of life, yet residents in many areas of the country lack accsess to or do not use broadband. To extend broadband access and adoption, the American Recovery and Reinvestment Act of 2009 (Recovery Act) provided over $7 billion to NTIA and RUS for grants or loans to support broadband projects. NTIA and RUS made all awards by September 30, 2010.

This report responds to mandates under the Recovery Act for GAO to examine the use of Recovery Act funds and report on the quarterly estimates of jobs funded. This report addresses (1) the progress of broadband projects, (2) their effect on expanding access to and adoption of broadband, and (3) any challenges awardees face in completing projects and agency actions to address these challenges. GAO analyzed program documentation and data and interviewed agency officials and BTOP and BIP awardees.

In: Rural Broadband   ISBN: 978-1-63463-215-7
Editor: Clyde L. Horn   © 2014 Nova Science Publishers, Inc.

Chapter 1

RECOVERY ACT: USDA SHOULD INCLUDE BROADBAND PROGRAM'S IMPACT IN ANNUAL PERFORMANCE REPORTS[*]

United States Government Accountability Office

WHY GAO DID THIS STUDY

Access to affordable broadband is seen as vital to economic growth and improved quality of life, yet its deployment in rural areas can be costly. The American Recovery and Reinvestment Act of 2009 (Recovery Act) appropriated funding for BIP, a USDA RUS program to fund broadband projects to provide service to end users in mostly rural areas. By 2010, RUS had awarded over $3 billion, primarily to 297 infrastructure projects, and required that projects be completed by June 2015 in approved areas.

GAO was asked to review BIP's results and impact. This report addresses (1) how RUS ensures that projects are completed by the deadline and as approved and (2) the extent to which RUS provides information to show BIP's impact. GAO interviewed RUS officials, reviewed policies, and analyzed RUS project data as of March 2014. GAO also interviewed five awardees from a nongeneralizable sample of seven BIP projects selected in part based on award size and location.

---

[*] This is an edited, reformatted and augmented version of the United States Government Accountability Office publication, GAO-14-511, dated June 2014.

WHAT GAO RECOMMENDS

GAO recommends that the Secretary of Agriculture include as part of the USDA annual performance plan and report, actual BIP results achieved against the updated subscribership goal. In commenting on a draft of this report, USDA said it agreed with the recommendation and will institute procedures to fully address it. USDA also provided technical comments, which were incorporated as appropriate.

WHAT GAO FOUND

The Rural Utilities Service (RUS) expects most Recovery Act-funded Broadband Initiatives Program (BIP) projects will be completed by the June 2015 deadline and as approved, but RUS faces challenges given the large scope of the program. As of March 2014, approximately 14 percent (42 of 297) of BIP infrastructure projects were terminated for a variety of reasons according to RUS officials, such as financial difficulties or inability to meet requirements. Of the 255 projects remaining, 87 percent were completed (39 projects) or partially operational (184 projects), meaning they provide service to some subscribers. To monitor projects and ensure they are completed within approved service areas, RUS relies on general field representatives to conduct in-person inspections and report monthly on project status. RUS officials said that they did not allow changes to service areas, but approved other types of changes such as changes in technology. GAO could not confirm this since RUS did not systematically track changes and did not provide GAO with information on project changes. Also, several challenges affect RUS's ability to oversee projects. For example, reduced staffing and travel funding levels during BIP's implementation will challenge RUS to complete inspections given the scope of the program, including 216 ongoing infrastructure projects to be completed by the June 2015 deadline.

RUS has reported limited information on BIP's impact since awarding funds to projects, and BIP results are not tracked in the Department of Agriculture's (USDA) annual performance reporting. Consequently, RUS has not shown how much the program's approximately $3 billion in project funding—an unprecedented level of federal investment in broadband—has affected broadband availability. RUS met the Recovery Act requirement to report to Congress quarterly until all funds were obligated. However, since the Recovery Act's reporting requirement ended, RUS has provided limited reporting on BIP program status and results during project implementation. A senior RUS official says RUS will now issue quarterly status reports until at least September 2015. USDA also has missed opportunities to report on BIP's impact as part of its annual performance plan and report. The GPRA Modernization Act of 2010 directs agencies to establish performance goals in annual performance plans and report the progress made toward these goals in annual performance reports. USDA's annual performance plan included a performance goal to provide new or improved broadband, but USDA did not include BIP results in its annual performance reports. USDA reported its BIP goal and results for fiscal year 2010 only and used the same estimate of BIP subscribership—developed before project execution—for both. RUS officials say the results were reported in fiscal year 2010 because that was the year funds were obligated. More recently, in March 2014, RUS updated the estimated number of subscribers from 847,239 to 728,733 to account for terminated projects. Reporting on and tracking BIP actual results against the updated goal is particularly important given that the majority of projects are ongoing and awardees are to continue to report the number of BIP subscribers added for at least 5 years after construction is completed. Without an updated performance goal and regular information reported on the results of BIP projects, it will be difficult for USDA, RUS, and policy makers to determine the impact of Recovery Act funds or BIP's progress on improving broadband availability.

ABBREVIATIONS

BCAS	Broadband Collection and Analysis System
BIP	Broadband Initiatives Program
CRS	Congressional Research Service
GFR	general field representative
OIG	Office of Inspector General
OMB	Office of Management and Budget
Recovery Act	American Recovery and Reinvestment Act of 2009
RUS	Rural Utilities Service
USDA	U.S. Department of Agriculture

June 17, 2014

The Honorable Fred Upton
Chairman
Committee on Energy and Commerce
House of Representatives

The Honorable Tim Murphy
Chairman
Subcommittee on Oversight and Investigations
Committee on Energy and Commerce
House of Representatives

The Honorable Greg Walden
Chairman
Subcommittee on Communications and Technology
Committee on Energy and Commerce
House of Representatives

Access to affordable broadband telecommunications[1] is increasingly viewed as vital to long-term economic growth and improved quality of life, just as electricity, telephone service, and the Interstate Highway System filled similar roles in previous generations. Sharing large amounts of information at ever greater speeds increases productivity, facilitates commerce, and drives innovation. Furthermore, broadband can improve citizens' quality of life. For example, broadband technology makes it possible for a patient to visit a local clinic and receive medical attention from specialists hundreds of miles away or for a student to access information not available from the local library. Broadband is particularly critical to provide advanced communications to remote communities and offer rural Americans new ways to participate in our economy and society.

To extend access to broadband throughout the United States, as well as to stimulate the economy and create jobs, Congress appropriated $7.2 billion for broadband programs under the American Recovery and Reinvestment Act of 2009 (Recovery Act).[2] This appropriation represented an unprecedented level of federal investment in expanding broadband. The $7.2 billion included $2.5 billion for the Broadband Initiatives Program (BIP) of the U.S. Department of Agriculture's (USDA) Rural Utilities Service (RUS), to provide loans, grants, and loan and grant combinations for broadband infrastructure projects primarily in rural areas.[3] In 2010, RUS awarded over \$3.5 billion to awardees for 320 BIP projects, primarily for projects expected to provide broadband service directly to end users in rural areas, including critical community facilities such as hospitals, libraries, and schools.[4]

This review responds to your request that we assess the results and impact of BIP to assist Congress in its ongoing oversight of Recovery Act broadband programs. This report also builds on our previous work on BIP.[5] In this report, we address: (1) how RUS ensures that funded projects are completed within required time frames and as approved, including within designated service areas, and (2) the extent to which RUS is providing information to show the program's impact on broadband availability. The information provided in this report also responds to a recurring mandate in the Recovery Act that we review bimonthly, the use of Recovery Act funds by recipients.[6]

To determine what actions RUS is taking to ensure that funded projects are completed within required time frames and as approved, including within designated service areas, we reviewed documents on RUS's monitoring policies and procedures and conducted interviews with RUS officials who oversee loan specialists, engineers, and general field representatives (GFR) who have BIP-related duties. We collected data from RUS on all BIP infrastructure projects, including completion status and disbursement of funds as of March 31, 2014. We assessed the reliability of this data by interviewing RUS officials about their databases and collection practices and reviewing relevant documentation, including guidance, descriptions of internal controls, and USDA Office of Inspector General (OIG) reviews. Based on this information, we determined that the data provided by RUS were sufficiently reliable for our reporting purposes. To further identify RUS's oversight actions, we selected seven (six ongoing and one completed) BIP infrastructure projects with approved service area locations throughout the United States based on criteria such as location, percentage of funds disbursed, and total award size. We selected ongoing projects to understand BIP's current oversight activities and one completed project in order to understand project impact. For each project we selected, we reviewed documents provided by RUS such as applications, award files, and quarterly visit reports. We also interviewed the RUS GFRs responsible for overseeing the projects and representatives from the awardees.[7]

To determine the extent to which RUS is providing information to show the program's impact on broadband availability, we reviewed publicly available RUS performance information such as BIP project directories, BIP quarterly reports and status reports, and USDA's annual performance plans and reports. We also reviewed previous GAO and USDA OIG reports on BIP performance goals and measures, including previous recommendations. To determine RUS's policies and procedures for collecting and reporting performance information and the agency's actions in response to recommendations made by USDA's OIG, we interviewed officials from RUS and USDA OIG. We also reviewed RUS's data collection policies and procedures and spoke with GFRs from the sample of seven projects, and awardee representatives from five of the seven, in regard to how they report, collect, and verify performance information. We also reviewed applicable criteria related to agency performance measurement and reporting, such as reporting provisions in the Recovery Act, associated Office of Management and Budget (OMB) guidance, and the GPRA Modernization Act of 2010,[8] which updated the Government Performance and Results Act of 1993.[9]

We conducted this performance audit from August 2013 to June 2014 in accordance with generally accepted government auditing standards. Those standards require that we plan and perform the audit to obtain sufficient, appropriate evidence to provide a reasonable basis for our findings and conclusions based on our audit objectives. We believe that the evidence obtained provides a reasonable basis for our findings and conclusions based on our audit objectives.

BACKGROUND

Rural areas tend to lag behind urban and suburban areas in broadband deployment. The provision of broadband Internet networks and services in the United States is generally privately financed. Rural areas, though, can have conditions that increase the cost of broadband deployment— such as remote areas with challenging terrain like mountains, which increase construction costs—or conditions that make it difficult to recoup deployment costs—such as relatively low population densities and incomes. These conditions make it less likely that a private service provider will build out or maintain a broadband network. Low population density can mean fewer potential subscribers, and low-income populations are less likely to use broadband. Other evidence suggests that rural low-income households are less likely to use broadband than metropolitan low-income households are.

However, because of broadband's perceived economic and social benefits, several federal programs aim to encourage its deployment, and the Recovery Act represented an unprecedented investment in this area.

Table 1. Summary of Rural Utilities Service's (RUS) Broadband Grant and Loan Programs

RUS program	Grant or loan	Purpose	Total appropriations, fiscal years 2003-2013
Rural Broadband Access Loan and Loan Guarantee Program	Loan	To fund the costs of the construction, improvement, and acquisition of facilities and equipment for broadband service in eligible rural communities.	$170 million[a]
Community Connect Grant Program	Grant	To provide broadband on a community-oriented basis to currently unserved rural areas to foster economic growth and deliver enhanced health care, education, and public safety services.	$125 million
Broadband Initiatives Program (BIP)	Loan, grant, and loan and grant combinations	To deploy infrastructure in rural areas, with an emphasis on infrastructure projects to provide service directly to end users.	$2.5 billion

Source: GAO analysis.

[a] During 2009 and 2010, the Rural Broadband Access Loan and Loan Guarantee Program was in hiatus while RUS implemented BIP.

To extend access to broadband and therefore increase rural economic opportunity, RUS finances broadband infrastructure deployment in rural areas. The BIP program represented an unprecedented federal investment in broadband deployment in general and for RUS in particular. Prior to the enactment of the Recovery Act, RUS's Rural Broadband Access Loan and Loan Guarantee and Community Connect programs were the only federal programs exclusively dedicated to deploying broadband infrastructure.[10] Together, these programs were appropriated a total of $295 million in the past decade (See table 1).[11] The $2.5 billion appropriated to BIP through the Recovery Act represented over eight times the federal investment in RUS broadband programs over the past decade.

BIP awardees must meet requirements set by the Recovery Act and RUS—such as requirements to deploy broadband infrastructure within and throughout service areas that are at least 75 percent rural—and regularly report information on progress to RUS. The Recovery Act authorized RUS to award grants, loans, and loan guarantees for broadband infrastructure in any area of the United States and mandated that areas to be served be at least 75 percent rural[12] without sufficient access to high-speed broadband service to facilitate rural economic development.[13] The rest of the project could be located in an area that was not rural. As a condition of the award, RUS requires BIP awardees to provide service to all customers who request and subscribe to its services within and throughout the approved service area. In addition, RUS officials say they require BIP awardees to submit quarterly financial and performance reports for at least 5 years after the completion of BIP projects. These quarterly reports, called Broadband Collection and Analysis System (BCAS) reports, require awardees to list detailed financial information and the number of subscribers in the approved service area.

Table 2. Broadband Initiatives Program Infrastructure Projects, 2010 to 2014

Date	Number of projects	Total funding (in millions)	Estimated results
Awarded as of September 2010	297	**$3,425**	847,239 subscribers will receive new or improved broadband service
Terminated as of December 2013	42	*$325*	
Updated as of March 2014	255	**$3,100**	728,733 subscribers will receive new or improved broadband service 61,047 fiber miles will be installed 1,391 wireless access points will be installed

Source: GAO analysis of RUS data.

By September 2010, RUS awarded $3.5 billion in BIP loans, grants, and loan and grant combinations to 320 projects, of which about $3.4 billion went to 297 infrastructure projects to enable service to end users such as households and businesses.[14] RUS solicited applications and made awards in two rounds, with the first round beginning in June 2009 and ending in April 2010, and the second round beginning in January 2010 and ending in September 2010. BIP awards went mainly to private-sector entities, including for-profit companies and cooperatives, to construct "last-mile" infrastructure projects, meaning a project that provides service directly to end users. Specifically, of the 297 infrastructure projects originally awarded, 267 were awarded to for-profit companies or cooperatives. In addition, 285 were last-mile projects, while the remaining 12 projects were middle-mile projects to provide a link from the Internet backbone to the last-mile networks of local providers that serve end users. RUS also funded 19 technical assistance and four satellite projects that accounted for approximately $103 million awarded.[15]

Based on information provided in the applications selected for award, in 2010 RUS estimated that 847,239 subscribers would receive new or improved broadband service through BIP infrastructure projects (see table 2). However, since the time of award to March 31, 2014, approximately 14 percent of the awarded BIP infrastructure projects (42 out of 297) were terminated. According to RUS officials, these projects were turned down by the awardee or terminated by RUS for a variety of reasons, such as awardee financial difficulties or inability to meet requirements. Consequently, in a BIP status report as of March 31, 2014, RUS updated its subscribership estimate goal to show that 728,733 subscribers were expected to receive new or improved broadband access as a result of BIP funding. According to RUS officials, this new number was calculated by removing the subscribership estimates attributed to terminated projects. In addition, after the terminated projects were removed, RUS estimated that 61,047 fiber miles and 1,391 wireless access points would be installed through BIP infrastructure projects.

BIP projects have encountered delays, and in response, RUS has pushed back the project completion deadline to shortly before funds expire in September 2015. Initially, when BIP grants and loans were awarded to projects in 2010, RUS stated that projects should be substantially completed within 2 years of award and should be fully completed within 3 years.[16] However, BIP projects generally follow a process that includes planning/contracting, construction, funding, and reporting phases (see figure 1). We previously found that some BIP projects experienced delays in the planning and contracting phase, such as delays in environmental reviews, securing permitting and rights-of-way agreements, and obtaining RUS approval of contracts and plans.[17] Projects also encountered challenges during construction due to severe weather or terrain and difficulty securing fiber due to a shortage. In response to these delays, in October 2011, RUS extended the BIP completion deadline to June 2015 to ensure that awardees could be reimbursed before the appropriation is closed on September 30, 2015.[18] In October 2011, RUS modified BIP requirements, requiring that construction commence within 180 days of the latter of the completion of the project's historic preservation or environmental reviews, and be fully completed no later than June 30, 2015. After September 30, 2015, the expired appropriation account will be closed and any balances remaining will be cancelled.

To address the challenge of overseeing the approximately 300 BIP projects and over $3 billion in funding, RUS hired temporary staff and a contractor. Before BIP implementation, RUS reported having 26 GFRs in fiscal year 2008. RUS awarded a contract to ICF International to assist with reviewing technical and financial materials and developing the post-award monitoring and reporting framework. In addition, RUS hired eight temporary GFRs to assist with the additional BIP workload. In August 2010, we recommended that USDA address the variability in funding levels for post-award oversight of BIP, given that the Recovery Act BIP funds could not be obligated after September 30, 2010, which ended the period of availability of the BIP appropriation.[19] In response, RUS extended its contract with ICF International through fiscal year 2013.[20] However, that contract and temporary staff appointments expired at the end of September 2013. As a result, fewer RUS staff, including engineers, loan specialists, and GFRs, are now responsible for BIP oversight. Since the contract ended on September 30, 2013, RUS has been transitioning the contractor's work back to RUS staff.

RUS'S OVERSIGHT INDICATES MOST PROJECTS WILL BE COMPLETED ON TIME AND AS APPROVED BUT FACES CHALLENGES GIVEN THE PROGRAM'S SCOPE

RUS Monitors BIP Projects and Expects Most Will Be Completed by the 2015 Deadline, but Awardees Face Challenges

RUS monitors projects and takes oversight actions through all BIP project phases, as shown in figure 2. For example, RUS engineers are responsible for ensuring that projects meet the specifications listed in applications and loan specialists are responsible for ensuring that projects are financially sustainable by reviewing funding requests and reporting.[21] Meanwhile, GFRs are the primary RUS point of contact for awardees and are responsible for collecting and reporting information on projects. For example, RUS GFRs submit monthly reports on projects' status and the number of fiber miles and wireless access points deployed.

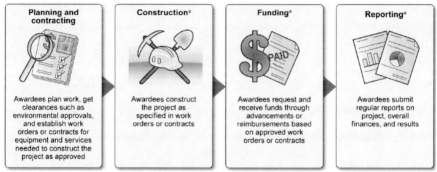

Planning and contracting	Construction[a]	Funding[a]	Reporting[a]
Awardees plan work, get clearances such as environmental approvals, and establish work orders or contracts for equipment and services needed to construct the project as approved	Awardees construct the project as specified in work orders or contracts	Awardees request and receive funds through advancements or reimbursements based on approved work orders or contracts	Awardees submit regular reports on project, overall finances, and results

[a] The construction, funding, and reporting phases occur concurrently.
Source: GAO analysis of Rural Utilities Service Information.

Figure 1. Phases of Broadband Initiatives Program Project Implementation.

Staff and role	Oversight actions by project phase			
	Planning and contracting	Construction[a]	Funding[a]	Reporting[a]
Engineers Ensure that projects are technically feasible and will meet specifications	Approve contracts to ensure work is aligned with application and meets requirements	Approve project changes, if any, to ensure results align with application	Check that work is in line with approved contracts before funds disbursed	None
Loan specialists Ensure projects and awardees are financially sustainable and loans (if any) can be repaid	None	None	Check that reporting and other requirements are met before funds disbursed	Review financial reporting to ensure project and awardee are financially sustainable
General field representatives Primary point of contact for awardees, inspect on site construction	Review and, in some cases, approve contracts	Conduct on-site inspections of construction	Review financial reporting by awardee	Collect information on projects and report monthly; verify information reported quarterly by awardee

[a] The construction, funding, and reporting phases occur concurrently.
Source: GAO analysis of Rural Utilities Service Information.

Figure 2. BIP's Oversight Activities by Project Phase and RUS Staff.

Based on GFR monthly reports, as of March 31, 2014, most projects were completed or partially operational. Specifically, 87 percent of the 255 BIP infrastructure projects were completed, meaning they were providing service throughout the entire approved service area, or were partially operational, meaning they were providing service to some subscribers in the approved service area (see table 3). Therefore, about 87 percent of BIP projects were beginning to offer broadband service to subscribers. However, since the partially operational projects had not yet been completed totally, as of this date, 216 projects, or about 85 percent of BIP infrastructure projects, were incomplete.

RUS also tracks projects by the amount of funding they have received, as RUS disburses funds to projects incrementally during implementation. As of March 31, 2014, RUS had disbursed about $2.2 billion, about 72 percent of the $3.1 billion in total BIP funds, to awardees. In addition, awardees of approximately 85 percent of the Recovery Act BIP infrastructure projects had received over half of the funds they had been awarded. The remaining approximately 15 percent have received less than half of the funds they had been awarded. However, the disbursement of funds by RUS does not fully reflect the amount of work completed on projects. RUS disburses BIP funds incrementally through advancements or reimbursements after awardees submit funding requests. Funding schedules vary among projects and can lag behind project construction. For example, representatives from one awardee told us that they are currently constructing a wireless tower and that given the nature of the contract, they would not be reimbursed by RUS until after construction was completed.

Table 3. BIP Infrastructure Project Status, as of March 31, 2014

Project status	Number of projects	Percentage of projects
Planning/ Contracting	0	0%
Construction	32	13%
Partially Operational	184	72%
Complete	39	15%
Total	**255[a]**	**100%**

Source: GAO analysis of RUS data.

[a] RUS originally awarded a total of 297 infrastructure projects and as of March 2014, 42 projects were terminated.

Based on data RUS tracks on project status and funds disbursed, RUS officials stated that they expect almost all BIP projects to be completed by the 2015 deadline. However, they predicted a small number of projects may have difficulty meeting the deadline due to project challenges and delays. RUS officials told us that because building out the entire service area was a condition of the original award agreement, awardees must use their own funds to complete the project if construction extends beyond the 2015 deadline. They also told us they are currently working with their Office of General Counsel to develop policies and potential actions in response to projects that have not built out the entire service area of the project by the 2015 deadline.

According to RUS officials and GFRs, current project delays were due to a variety of challenges, some of which the awardee and RUS have limited options to overcome. These challenges include lengthy environmental reviews, weather, compliance with reporting requirements, and approval of contracts and plans.[22] To address these challenges, awardees have tried to construct projects in compressed time frames but can encounter further construction delays, such as weather. For example, representatives from one awardee we spoke to noted that environmental review delays caused the project to miss an entire construction season, while subsequent seasons were shortened due to severe weather. Additionally, RUS officials reported that some awardees faced financial challenges. For example, according to a GFR, one BIP project was struggling due in part to the awardee's overall financial problems. The GFR noted that RUS was limited in taking action against the awardee, since holding back BIP funds would only make the financial problems worse, putting the project further at risk.

Awardees who were unfamiliar with RUS's processes encountered particular challenges and delays. We previously found that, according to RUS officials, BIP awardees that had not received funding from RUS in the past were more likely to experience difficulties complying with reporting requirements than those awardees with a history of borrowing from RUS.[23] Although 38 percent of the original 297 BIP infrastructure projects went to new awardees that had not previously received funding from RUS, we found these projects made up a majority of projects terminated (64 percent). RUS officials and GFRs told us that new awardees faced continued challenges complying with RUS's reporting and contracting requirements. Representatives from one such new awardee we spoke to, a local government entity, noted they faced challenges in filing BCAS reports regularly because their financial systems were not designed to produce the information required on a quarterly basis. These BCAS reporting problems resulted in RUS withholding funding, and consequently, project delays. Representatives from another new RUS awardee said they were a small company that was unable to handle the additional BIP workload and, as a result, hired an outside consultant to handle the required reporting. To help address these challenges, RUS GFRs have provided additional assistance to new awardees. For example, a GFR we spoke to told us he reminded a new awardee of BIP reporting requirements. In another case, GFRs we spoke to worked to ensure that a new awardee's contracts met RUS requirements by acting as a liaison to RUS headquarters staff to help resolve issues.

RUS Expects That Projects Will Be Completed as Approved, but Faces Challenges Given Scope of Program

RUS's Oversight Processes to Ensure Projects Are Completed as Approved

RUS takes several steps to ensure projects are completed as approved. First, according to RUS officials and GFRs, RUS did not allow projects to make changes to the approved service areas specified in their applications. RUS officials expect all projects to provide service within and throughout the areas specified in their applications. However, in some cases, RUS officials said they approved other types of project changes. We were unable to assess the nature of project changes because RUS did not systematically track them and did not provide us with a list of all project changes.[24] Second, as mentioned earlier, RUS also has a framework of oversight activities in place to ensure projects are completed as specified in their applications (see figure 2). As part of its overall oversight framework, RUS relies on GFRs located throughout the country to verify that project construction and subsequent service are within and throughout approved service areas. GFRs are generally assigned to BIP projects based on the state where the project or awardee is located. GFRs monitor the implementation and status of project build-out through three steps, as described below:

1. *Ongoing construction inspections*: RUS requires GFRs to conduct construction inspections to confirm that BIP funds are used for approved purposes and within the designated service areas. Through

periodic inspections, GFRs verify the work is aligned with the approved application. The frequency of these inspections depends on factors such as whether construction is active on site to inspect. GFRs we interviewed described various ways they inspected construction. For example, one GFR we spoke to described how he tracked planned and completed construction on a map to ensure the awardee was building within the approved service area. Another GFR we spoke to mentioned viewing equipment installed, such as the placement of fiber cables, to verify the construction was within the service area.

2. *Verification of subscribership:* RUS requires GFRs to review and verify that the subscribership numbers reported by awardees are reasonable. Once BIP project awardees begin signing up customers, they submit subscribership numbers to RUS quarterly through BCAS. GFRs we interviewed described various ways they verify the awardee-reported subscribership numbers. For instance, a GFR told us he requested copies of billing records from an awardee to verify that subscribers were located within the project's service area. Another GFR we spoke to stated that he confirmed subscribership by traveling throughout the project service area and viewing the placement of equipment on subscribers' property.

3. *Final project closeout inspections:* As part of the closeout process, RUS requires GFRs to conduct a final inspection to ensure that service is available throughout the approved service area. RUS instructs GFRs to test service throughout the service area, including areas difficult to reach, and to interview local residents and businesses regarding the service. If GFRs find any problems with service coverage, they will investigate other areas within the service area and bring any issues to the attention of RUS management. RUS officials told us that as of April 2014, they had conducted approximately 25 closeout inspections out of about 40 completed projects. GFRs we spoke to described various ways they plan to verify the service availability in the approved service area. For example, one GFR told us he will test the availability of wireless service by using a smart phone to test the signal strength in multiple locations within the service area. Another GFR told us he will proactively reach out to residents in the service area to solicit feedback on service quality and availability to ensure service was being provided at the level indicated in the awarded application.

As mentioned above, RUS officials said they did not allow changes to project service areas although they did allow other types of changes, such as changes in technology. However, we were unable to verify this because RUS did not provide us with any information about these changes. According to RUS officials, awardees could request project changes, which RUS engineers reviewed and approved on a case-by-case basis. RUS engineers told us they evaluated requested changes based on the approved application and budget, with a focus on whether the proposed change affected the access to or speed of broadband service. RUS documented project change decisions in letters to awardees. However, RUS does not have policies on the types of changes allowed or a master list of changes considered, and did not provide us with a list of projects with approved changes. As a result, we could not evaluate these changes. According to RUS officials, less than 15 projects made significant changes for reasons such as updates in technology. For example, representatives from one awardee told us they changed their project because the equipment specified in their application was no longer available. Representatives from another awardee said they changed the design of their project to include one less wireless tower to provide the same level of service at a lower cost than was proposed in their application.

Challenges to RUS's Oversight Processes

Despite these oversight processes, RUS faces challenges ensuring that all projects are completed as approved for the following reasons.

1. *Reduced RUS Staffing:* RUS staffing resources have been reduced while BIP projects are ongoing, and as a result, staff workload has increased. In 2009 and 2010, we found that RUS's ability to oversee BIP projects faced challenges because it lacked sufficient staff and resources, among other reasons.[25] RUS officials stated that they did not request or receive additional funds to cover administrative costs beyond funding appropriated by the Recovery Act. Furthermore, most of the eight temporary GFRs RUS hired to assist with BIP oversight left when their terms ended in September 2013, while some were hired as permanent GFRs, according to RUS officials. RUS now has approximately the same number of GFRs as before the Recovery Act was enacted, but has an increased workload given that 216 BIP projects were still ongoing as of March 2014. Specifically, RUS officials report that there were 26 GFRs in fiscal year 2008 before BIP implementation, and that as of April 2014, RUS had 25 GFRs and 2

vacancies. GFRs are now responsible for BIP projects previously overseen by temporary GFRs, in addition to the other projects they oversee, such as projects from the Community Connect Grant Program and the Rural Broadband Access Loan and Loan Guarantee Program.

2. *Reduced Travel Funds:* RUS has also faced challenges overseeing BIP projects with reduced travel funds. At a minimum, RUS requires GFRs to conduct visits quarterly, which can be conducted in-person or remotely through a teleconference. In-person visits can take place at the project's service area location or at the awardee's offices or headquarters when the offices are in a different location from the project. GFRs we spoke to overseeing six of the seven projects we examined noted that reduced travel funds have been a challenge. GFRs noted reduced travel funds resulted in fewer in-person visits to the project than on a quarterly basis in some cases. For example, GFRs overseeing one of the seven projects in our sample had conducted visits with the awardees' headquarters, but had not yet conducted an in-person inspection of the project service areas. A senior RUS official said that although funding has been limited at times throughout BIP implementation, such as the end of budget cycles, RUS is not concerned about there being sufficient travel funds to conduct the needed BIP closeout visits.

3. *Scope of Work Remaining:* Given that BIP projects must be completed within one year, RUS faces challenges in completing its oversight processes, including a final in-person closeout inspection to verify service availability, for all projects as they finish construction. As mentioned previously, RUS officials said that as of April 2014, RUS had completed about 25 closeout inspections among approximately 40 completed projects. Given that an additional 216 BIP infrastructure projects were ongoing (under construction or partially operational) as of March 2014, GFRs will have numerous closeout inspections to complete in a short time frame. A RUS senior official noted that GFRs will likely continue conducting closeout inspections beyond the 2015 deadline.

GFR on-site inspections are RUS's key oversight mechanism for ensuring that remote areas are built out as planned and that Recovery Act funds reach hard-to-serve rural areas. We have previously concluded that companies may have an incentive to build first where they have the most opportunity for profit and leave the more remote parts of their projects for last in order to achieve the highest number of subscribers as possible.[26]

As the deadline for the BIP program nears, some awardees may be stretched to complete remaining construction. While awardees try to complete their projects before the Recovery Act BIP appropriation is closed, RUS may likewise be stretched to complete close out inspections with fewer staff than when the Recovery Act was enacted and with limited travel funds to visit projects throughout their territories, which can cover thousands of miles and multiple states. To help address these challenges, RUS plans to monitor projects beyond the 2015 deadline to ensure service is provided throughout the approved service area. RUS officials stated that they are currently working with their Office of General Counsel to explore options to take regarding awardees that have not provided service throughout the approved service area by the September 2015 deadline.

RUS COLLECTS BIP'S PERFORMANCE INFORMATION BUT PROVIDES LIMITED REPORTING OF PROGRAM'S IMPACT

RUS Collects and Has Provided Limited Reporting of BIP Performance Information Despite Efforts to Improve Reliability

Although RUS collects performance information to measure BIP's impact on broadband subscribership, it has provided limited reporting of this information. OMB's Recovery Act guidance required federal agencies to measure specific program outcomes, supported by corresponding quantifiable output measures.[27] To this end, RUS requires awardees to submit quarterly BCAS reports on the number of households, businesses, educational providers, libraries, health care providers, and public safety providers subscribing to new or improved broadband service through BIP.

Although RUS has met the Recovery Act reporting requirements, it has provided limited reporting on BIP program status and results during project implementation. However, it plans to now publish reports quarterly until at least September 2015. The Recovery Act required that RUS submit quarterly reports to Congress on the use of BIP funds until all funds were obligated.[28] Further, OMB guidance calls for federal agencies to report the public benefits of Recovery Act funds clearly, accurately, and in a timely manner.[29] As required by the Recovery Act, RUS provided quarterly reports to Congress during the period while BIP's funding was being obligated. From May 2009 through December 2010, RUS published seven quarterly reports on its website. These quarterly reports detailed RUS's actions to obligate BIP funds, including information on the funding announcements and obligated awards. Since then, RUS status reporting has been limited and inconsistent. Specifically, since December 2010, RUS has issued three status reports, reporting data as of April 3, 2013; August 26, 2013; and March 31, 2014. These reports have included performance results, including the number of households, businesses, educational providers, libraries, health care providers, and public safety providers subscribing to new or improved broadband service through BIP. Beginning with the March 2014 report, RUS intends to publish reports quarterly until the end of fiscal year 2015, according to a senior official. This official noted that if BIP does not appear to have met its subscribership goals by then, RUS may consider continuing to publish quarterly reports given that projects will continue to add, and awardees will continue to report, BIP subscribers for at least 5 years after projects are completed. A senior RUS official previously noted that projects will continue to add subscribers for years after completing construction.

In addition, BIP status reports have previously contained information that was determined unreliable by GAO and USDA's OIG, although RUS is taking steps to improve reliability, according to officials. RUS's BIP status reports have included subscribership information such as the number of households, businesses, and libraries receiving new or improved broadband service as a result of BIP. In September 2012, we found that this subscribership information was inaccurate and that RUS was taking steps to improve it.[30] Despite these efforts by RUS, in August 2013, the USDA OIG found some BIP performance information unreliable and that RUS lacked adequate controls to ensure the reliability of the data. USDA's OIG recommended that RUS revise the BCAS guidance for awardees and staff and provide detailed and clear instructions on the entry and review of BIP performance data in BCAS.[31] In response to this recommendation, according to a senior RUS official and USDA OIG officials, RUS is developing guidance and anticipates this corrective action will be implemented in June 2014. This could improve the reliability of subsequent reports.

In addition, RUS does not track subscribership by rural area and, as a result, is not able to show the impact of the BIP program on rural broadband availability. The OIG previously found that RUS's performance information makes it impossible to measure BIP's impact in rural areas because the information was not collected by rural area. The Recovery Act required that

BIP service areas be at least 75 percent rural without sufficient access to high-speed broadband service to facilitate economic development. The rest of the project area may not be rural. According to a RUS official, very little of projects' service areas were non-rural. Despite this, BIP awardees may potentially attract subscribers disproportionately in the non-rural areas of the service area. Therefore, BIP's subscribership measures do not indicate the extent to which Recovery Act funding was used to deploy broadband access in rural areas. To address this gap, OIG recommended that RUS report performance data that directly measure the impact of each award on the expansion of broadband service in rural areas. In its response to OIG, RUS reported it that cannot report this level of detailed information because it was not specified that way in RUS's agreements with its awardees. RUS further indicated that since BIP is a one-time program, it does not believe using taxpayers' funding to make substantial changes to its reporting system in order to collect subscribership information in rural areas would be appropriate. In response, USDA's OIG accepted RUS's management decision.

USDA Annual Performance Reports Do Not Track BIP's Performance Against a Related Goal

In addition, USDA has missed opportunities to report on BIP's impact. Over the life of the BIP program, USDA's annual performance reports have not tracked BIP's performance results against a goal. The GPRA Modernization Act requires that each year agencies establish performance goals in performance plans and provide an update by comparing actual performance achieved against performance goals in annual performance reports.[32] Regarding a goal related to BIP, although USDA performance reports identified expanding broadband access as a goal, they did not include BIP. For example, USDA's most recent annual performance report, from fiscal year 2013, and its most recent performance plan, for fiscal year 2015, listed the "number of borrowers/subscribers receiving new or improved telecommunications services" as a performance goal. This goal was listed under a strategic objective to "enhance rural prosperity." The numbers reported under this annual performance goal did not include BIP and instead included other RUS programs, such as the Rural Broadband Access Loan and Loan Guarantee program. A USDA official told us that BIP performance was not included in USDA's annual performance report because it was part of the Recovery Act reports. However, as mentioned previously, RUS is no longer required under the Recovery Act to provide reports. Regarding reporting on BIP performance, instead of reporting actual results, RUS reported its performance goal, or estimate of BIP subscribership, as results. Specifically, in fiscal year 2010, USDA reported the 847,239 subscribers that it anticipates will receive new or improved broadband service as results.[33] As previously reported by the USDA OIG, RUS officials said the results were reported in fiscal year 2010 because that was the year the funds were obligated. As we found in 2012, this total did not reflect actual program results, because it was calculated by RUS using estimates contained in applications and developed prior to the execution of the funded projects.[34] Further, the estimated number of subscribers to receive new or improved service through BIP that RUS reported in fiscal year 2010—847,239—is now out of date given that as of March 31, 2014, RUS reduced this estimate to 728,733, as we explained earlier in this report.

Given the amount of funding devoted to BIP, having information on BIP's actual performance is important for determining the program's effectiveness. By not reporting annually on BIP's actual performance, USDA is not demonstrating the impact of Recovery Act funds and BIP's progress on improving broadband availability. Without this information, future efforts to expand broadband may lack important information on the types of projects that were most effective at meeting subscribership goals, thereby limiting the ability to apply federal resources to programs with the best likelihood of success.

CONCLUSION

BIP represented an unprecedented level of federal investment in broadband infrastructure, amounting to over eight times the funds RUS otherwise had available for broadband in the past decade. RUS collects and is taking steps to improve the reliability of BIP performance information. However, BIP's reporting has been limited and is not reflected in USDA annual performance reports. As a result, RUS has not shown how the approximately $3 billion in funds awarded to BIP projects have affected broadband availability. Reporting on and tracking the number of subscribers receiving service through BIP is particularly important given that the majority of projects are ongoing and that projects are to continue to add, and awardees are to continue to report, BIP subscribers for at least 5 years after construction is completed. Without reliable and regular information on the results of BIP projects, it will be difficult for USDA, RUS, and policy makers to determine the impact of Recovery Act funds and BIP's progress on improving broadband availability. Without this information, future efforts to expand broadband may lack important information on the types of projects that were most effective at meeting subscribership goals, thereby limiting the ability to apply federal resources to programs with the best likelihood of success.

RECOMMENDATION

To provide information on the impact of federal investments in expanding broadband infrastructure, we recommend the Secretary of Agriculture include BIP performance information as part of the USDA's annual performance plan and report by comparing actual results achieved against the current subscribership goal.

AGENCY COMMENTS

We provided a draft of this report to the Secretary of Agriculture for review and comment. In an email received June 4, 2014, a Management Analyst with USDA on behalf of USDA Rural Development stated that RUS generally agreed with the report and its recommendation and will institute procedures to fully address the recommendation. However, RUS cited concerns that our discussion of RUS's requirement to serve the entire service area in the context of design changes may give the impression that project service areas were not completely served. RUS stated this is a mischaracterization and that, although it does not have a master list of considered project changes or policies on the types of changes allowed, it does have information on changes that were approved. However, RUS stated it did not provide us with this information because the effort to provide it would not be efficient. In response, we clarified language in the report to indicate that RUS did not—rather than could not—provide the information. RUS also provided technical comments, which we incorporated as appropriate.

Mark L. Goldstein
Director, Physical Infrastructure Issues

APPENDIX I: OBJECTIVES, SCOPE, AND METHODOLOGY

This report discusses (1) how the Rural Utilities Service (RUS) ensures that funded Broadband Initiatives Program (BIP) projects are completed within required time frames and as approved, including within designated service areas and (2) the extent to which RUS is providing information to show the program's impact on broadband availability.

To determine how RUS ensures that funded BIP infrastructure projects are completed within required time frames and as approved, including within designated service areas, we collected and analyzed documents from RUS on its monitoring policies and procedures. This information included RUS policies and guidance on general field representative (GFR) quarterly visits and monthly reporting, contracting and disbursement of funds procedures, and awardee Broadband Collection and Analysis System (BCAS) instructions. We conducted interviews with RUS officials who oversee loan specialists, engineers, and GFRs with BIP-related duties. We also reviewed previous reports on BIP oversight from GAO, US Department of Agriculture's (USDA) Office of Inspector General (OIG), and the Congressional Research Service (CRS).

To determine how RUS tracks infrastructure project completion, describes the status of all infrastructure projects, and characterizes the types of projects terminated and ongoing, we collected and analyzed data from RUS on all BIP projects as of December 2013 and summary data as of March 31, 2014. The data as of December 2013 included the size of award, completion status, location (state) of designated or approved service area, whether the awardee had previously received RUS funding, and amount of funds disbursed. We later updated this information by collecting summary data from RUS as of March 31, 2014. To determine the reliability of RUS data, we reviewed relevant documentation— including guidance, descriptions of internal controls, and USDA's OIG reviews—and interviewed RUS officials about their databases and collection practices. Based on this information, we determined that the data provided to us were sufficiently reliable for our reporting purposes.

To further characterize RUS's oversight actions, we selected a nongeneralizable sample of six ongoing infrastructure projects and one completed project. We selected ongoing projects to understand BIP's current oversight activities and one completed project in order to understand project impact. First, we initially selected two infrastructure projects, one completed and one ongoing. These projects were selected based on factors such as the total size of the award, number of premises proposed to be served, and not covered by previous GAO or USDA's OIG audit work. Both projects' approved service areas were in Michigan. We then selected an additional five projects that were not substantially completed, according to RUS's definition (having received less than 67 percent of BIP funds disbursed), and were not previously sampled by previous USDA OIG or GAO audit work. We selected case study projects based on: approved service area location; total award size; percentage of BIP funds disbursed as of December 2013; type of broadband technology (wireline or wireless); and awardee type (for example, for-profit company or state or local government). We selected infrastructure projects dispersed throughout the US with approved service areas in Pennsylvania, South Carolina, Iowa, Texas, and Nevada. The sample of infrastructure projects we chose is not representative of all BIP projects. For each selected case-study project, we reviewed documentation provided by RUS such as award applications, grant or loan agreements, letters documenting project changes (if any), and GFR quarterly visit reports. In addition, we interviewed GFRs assigned to each case study project and representatives from the awardee.[35]

To determine the extent to which RUS is providing information to show the program's impact on broadband availability, we reviewed publicly available RUS performance information, such as BIP project directories, BIP quarterly and status reports, and USDA annual performance plans and reports. We also reviewed previous GAO, CRS, and USDA OIG reports on BIP performance measures, including previous recommendations regarding RUS performance information. To determine RUS's policies and procedures for collecting and reporting performance information and the agency's actions in response to recommendations made by USDA OIG, we interviewed officials from RUS and USDA OIG. We also reviewed RUS's data collection policies and procedures and spoke with GFRs from the seven case studies and awardee representatives from five of the seven, in regard to how they report, collect, and verify performance information. We also reviewed applicable criteria related to agency performance measurement and reporting, such as reporting provisions in the American Recovery and Reinvestment Act of 2009,[36] associated Office of Management and Budget (OMB) guidance, and the GPRA Modernization Act of 2010.[37]

We conducted this performance audit from August 2013 to June 2014 in accordance with generally accepted government auditing standards. Those standards require that we plan and perform the audit to obtain sufficient, appropriate evidence to provide a reasonable basis for our findings and conclusions based on our audit objectives. We believe that the evidence obtained provides a reasonable basis for our findings and conclusions based on our audit objectives.

End Notes

[1] The term broadband commonly refers to high-speed Internet access. GAO, *Telecommunications: Broadband Deployment Is Extensive throughout the United States, but It Is Difficult to Assess the Extent of Deployment Gaps in Rural Areas*, GAO-06-426 (Washington, D.C.: May 5, 2006).

[2] Pub. L. No. 111-5, 123 Stat. 115 (2009).

[3] *Recovery Act,* div. A, title I, 123 Stat., 118-119. The Recovery Act also included $4.7 billion for the Department of Commerce's National Telecommunications and Information Administration to create the Broadband Technology Opportunities Program to expand broadband services.

[4] Because of provisions in the Federal Credit Reform Act of 1990, 2 U.S.C. § 661a(5)(F), RUS may award grants and loans that exceed its budgetary authority. Because loans, unlike grants, must be repaid to the government with interest, RUS is required to account for the budgetary impact of loans by estimating the expected net loss (or gain) of loans. This net amount, which is estimated by calculating the net present value of all cash flows to and from RUS over the lifetime of the loans, is referred to as the subsidy cost of the loans. RUS must charge the cost of any grants plus the subsidy cost of loans against its budget authority.

[5] GAO, *Recovery Act: Broadband Programs Are Ongoing, and Agencies' Efforts Would Benefit from Improved Data Quality*, GAO-12-937 (Washington, D.C.: Sept. 14, 2012); *Recovery Act: Broadband Program Awards and Risks to Oversight*, GAO-11-371T (Washington, D.C.: Feb. 10, 2011); *Recovery Act: Further Opportunities Exist to Strengthen Oversight of Broadband Stimulus Programs*, GAO-10-823 (Washington, D.C.: Aug. 4, 2010); and *Recovery Act: Agencies Are Addressing Broadband Program Challenges, but Actions Are Needed to Improve Implementation*, GAO-10-80 (Washington, D.C.: Nov. 16, 2009).

[6] *Recovery Act*, div. A, title IX, § 901, 123 Stat.,191. Updates on GAO's oversight of Recovery Act funds can be found at: http://gao.gov/recovery.

[7] We spoke to representatives from five of the seven awardees we selected. The remaining two awardees did not respond to our requests to be interviewed.

[8] Pub. L. No. 111-352, 124 Stat. 3866 (2011).

[9] Pub. L. No. 103-62, 107 Stat. 285 (1993).

[10] GAO has ongoing work related to the Rural Broadband Access Loan and Loan Guarantee program that is expected to be released in June 2014.

[11] For the Rural Broadband Access Loan and Loan Guarantee Program, the direct appropriation covers the loan subsidy. Congress also approves a specific loan level or lending authority for the program, a level that has generally been much higher than the loan subsidy amount. For example, in fiscal year 2012, the direct appropriation was $6 million but the lending authority was $212 million.

[12] Recovery Act, div. A, title I, 123 Stat.,118-119. For purposes of BIP, rural area is "any area, as confirmed by the 2000 census, which is not located within (1) a city, town, or incorporated area that has a population of greater than 20,000 inhabitants or (2) an urbanized area contiguous and adjacent to a city or town that has a population of greater than 50,000 inhabitants. For purposes of the definition of rural area, urbanized area means a densely

populated territory as defined by the latest decennial census. 74 Fed. Reg. 33104, 33109 (July 9, 2009).

[13] In the first-round Notice of Funds Availability for BIP, RUS defined broadband as providing a two-way data transmission with advertised speeds of at least 768 kilobits per second (kbps) downstream and at least 200 kbps upstream to end users. In the second-round Notice for BIP, the definition was changed to service at the rate of 5 megabits per second (upstream and downstream combined).

[14] The amount of funds awarded by RUS exceeds its appropriation because RUS can award and obligate funds in excess of its budget authority through the use of loans.

[15] As of March 31, 2014, all satellite and technical assistance projects were completed. The remainder of this report will be focused on infrastructure projects.

[16] A BIP project was required to be substantially complete no later than 2 years after award and was considered to be substantially complete once an awardee had received 67 percent of its award funds. 74 Fed. Reg., 33110.

[17] GAO-12-937.

[18] Appropriations available for definite periods close 5 years after the period of availability has expired as provided by 31 U.S.C. § 1552(a).

[19] See GAO-10-823; *Recovery Act*, div. A, § 1603, 123 Stat., 302.

[20] See GAO-11-371T.

[21] In addition, according to RUS officials, field accountants are responsible for reviewing BIP grant and loan transactions and annual awardee financial audits to ensure that BIP funds are used for allowable activities. Field accountants are part of the Program Accounting Services Division of Rural Development, which conducts loan fund and accounting reviews of Rural Development electric and telecommunications borrowers.

[22] In an earlier review that included BIP, we found that similar challenges contributed to project delays. See GAO-12-937.

[23] GAO-12-937.

[24] RUS did not provide us with this information because RUS officials said that the effort to provide it would not be efficient since it did not have a master list of considered project changes.

[25] GAO-10-823 and GAO-10-80.

[26] GAO-10-823.

[27] OMB Memorandum M-09-10, Initial Implementing Guidance for the American Recovery and Reinvestment Act of 2009 (February 18, 2009).

[28] Recovery Act, div. A, title XVI, 123 Stat., 118-119.

[29] OMB Memorandum M-09-10.

[30] GAO-12-937.

[31] See USDA OIG, *American Recovery and Reinvestment Act of 2009—Broadband Initiatives Program—Post-Award Controls*, Audit Report -9703-0002-32 (Washington, D.C.: Aug. 22, 2013).

[32] Pub. L. No. 111-352, § 3,124 Stat. 3866, 3867 (2011), amending 31 U.S.C. § 1115.

[33] This was previously reported by USDA's OIG. See USDA OIG, *American Recovery and Reinvestment Act of 2009- Broadband Initiatives Program- Post-Award Controls*, Audit Report -9703-0002-32 (Washington, D.C.: Aug. 22, 2013).

[34] GAO-12-937.

[35] We spoke to representatives from five of the seven awardees we selected. The remaining two awardees did not respond to our requests to be interviewed.

[36] Pub. L. No. 111-5, 123 Stat. 115 (2009).

[37] Pub. L. No. 111-352, 124 Stat. 3866 (2011).

In: Rural Broadband   ISBN: 978-1-63463-215-7
Editor: Clyde L. Horn   © 2014 Nova Science Publishers, Inc.

Chapter 2

TELECOMMUNICATIONS: USDA SHOULD EVALUATE THE PERFORMANCE OF THE RURAL BROADBAND LOAN PROGRAM[*]

United States Government Accountability Office

WHY GAO DID THIS STUDY

Access to affordable broadband telecommunications is increasingly viewed as vital to economic growth and improved quality of life. Broadband is particularly critical in rural areas, where advanced communications can reduce the isolation of remote communities and individuals. To extend access to broadband and therefore increase economic opportunity in rural America, RUS finances the construction of broadband through a loan program.

GAO was asked to assess issues related to the loan program. This report addresses the (1) geographic distribution and financial performance of loans and (2) relationship between loans and broadband deployment and economic development, and how USDA evaluates progress towards these outcomes.

To address these research questions, GAO interviewed broadband providers and stakeholders selected for their varying experiences, including those that have and have not received RUS loans. GAO also analyzed RUS

---

[*] This is an edited, reformatted and augmented version of the United States Government Accountability Office publication, GAO-14-471, dated May 2014.

and U.S. Census Bureau data from 2003— 2013 as well as the most recent National Broadband Map data.

WHAT GAO RECOMMENDS

GAO recommends that USDA (1) evaluate loans made by RUS through the loan program to identify characteristics of loans that may be at risk of rescission or default and (2) align the goals in its *APR* to the loan program's purpose, to the extent feasible. In commenting on a draft of this report, USDA said it will strive to fully implement the report's recommendations.

WHAT GAO FOUND

The U.S. Department of Agriculture (USDA) Rural Utilities Service (RUS) has approved 100 loans to geographically and demographically diverse areas through its Rural Broadband Access Loan and Loan Guarantee Program ("loan program"), though over 40 percent of these loans are no longer active. The geographic distribution of RUS loans is widespread, with broadband providers in 43 states having received one or more loans through the loan program from 2003 through 2013. About $2 billion in loans have been made to providers in areas with diverse demographics and economies, including areas with low population densities and income as well as areas in relative proximity to large cities with robust local economies. Of the 100 RUS loans approved through the loan program, 48 are currently being repaid, and 9 have been fully paid back. Forty-three are no longer active, either because they were cancelled before they were paid out (25 rescinded) or because the provider defaulted by failing to abide by the terms of the loan (18 defaulted). Approving a loan requires significant resources. Loans that default or are rescinded can represent an inefficient use of RUS resources. Despite these issues, RUS has not gathered information or performed analysis to better understand what might lead a project to default or otherwise make a project a poor candidate for receiving a loan. Federal guidance, though, emphasizes the importance of assessing the risk associated with loan programs.

RUS loans can help promote limited broadband deployment and economic development, but USDA's performance goals do not fully align with the loan program's purpose. According to GAO analysis of National Broadband Map deployment data as of June 2013, areas with RUS loans generally have the same number of broadband providers as areas without a loan. However, the RUS loan program can enhance the quality and reach of broadband networks in rural areas, according to stakeholders. Further, according to GAO analysis of RUS loans and U.S. Census Bureau data from 2003 through 2011—the years for which RUS and relevant Census data are available—areas affected by at least one approved RUS loan were associated with modestly higher levels of employment and payroll (1 to 4 percent) after the year of loan approval and in all subsequent years, as compared to areas that did not receive RUS loans. As stated in the program regulations, the purpose of the RUS loan program is to increase broadband deployment (that is, the number of broadband subscribers with access to new or improved broadband service) and economic opportunity in rural America through the provision of broadband services. USDA's *Annual Performance Report (APR)* provides information on the achievements of USDA's programs each fiscal year. The goals in USDA's report, though, do not fully align with the purpose of the loan program. For instance, USDA's *APR* does not have any goals or measures to determine the loan program's progress towards economic development outcomes. As our past work has shown, an attribute of a successful performance goal is whether it aligns with division and agency-wide goals. Agency performance goals that do not link to program goals can lead to incentives and behaviors that do not support the achievement of division or agency-wide goals. Performance goals aligned with the program's purpose may help USDA and Congress better monitor the outcomes of the loan program.

ABBREVIATIONS

APR	*Annual Performance Report*
CAF	Connect America Fund
FCC	Federal Communications Commission
ICC	Intercarrier Compensation
NBM	National Broadband Map
OMB	Office of Management and Budget
RUCA	Rural-Urban Commuting Area
RUS	Rural Utilities Service
USDA	U.S. Department of Agriculture
USF	Universal Service Fund

May 22, 2014

The Honorable Debbie Stabenow
Chairwoman
The Honorable Thad Cochran
Ranking Member
Committee on Agriculture, Nutrition and Forestry
United States Senate

The Honorable Pat Roberts
United States Senate

Access to affordable broadband telecommunications[1] is increasingly viewed as vital to long-term economic growth and improved quality of life, just as electricity, telephone, and interstate highway systems filled similar roles in previous generations. The ability to share large amounts of information at ever-greater speeds increases productivity, facilitates commerce, and drives innovation. Furthermore, broadband can improve citizens' quality of life. For example, broadband technology makes it possible for a patient to visit a local clinic and receive medical attention from specialists hundreds of miles away, for a student to access information not available from the local library, and for a firefighter to download blueprints of a burning building and intervene appropriately. Broadband is particularly critical in rural areas, where advanced communications can reduce the isolation of remote communities and individuals.

To extend access to broadband and therefore increase economic opportunity in rural America, the U.S. Department of Agriculture's (USDA) Rural Utilities Service (RUS) finances the construction of broadband infrastructure through RUS's Rural Broadband Access Loan and Loan Guarantee Program ("loan program"). The repayment status and geographic distribution of loans approved through this program have not been widely reported to date. The relationship, if any, between these loans and desired outcomes such as broadband deployment and economic development is also not well understood. Some stakeholders have also expressed concern about the impact of recent Federal Communications Commission (FCC) reforms to the Universal Service Fund (USF) and Intercarrier Compensation (ICC) systems on the RUS broadband loan program.[2] The USF in particular has functioned as an ongoing subsidy for telecommunications providers, and according to some providers, reductions in USF support could jeopardize the ability of those providers to pay back or take out RUS loans.

You asked us to review the distribution and status of loans as well as the effects of these loans. This report addresses: (1) the geographic distribution and financial performance of loans since 2002; (2) the relationship, if any, between loans and broadband deployment and economic development in rural areas, and how USDA evaluates progress toward these outcomes; and (3) the impact of reforms to the USF High-Cost program and ICC on the RUS broadband loan program.

To examine the geographic distribution and financial performance of loans since 2002, we gathered and analyzed RUS loan data. Specifically, we collected information on the recipient, approval date, amount, repayment status, as well as the proposed technology and communities to be served by the project for each loan approved by RUS since the program's authorization in 2002. We also collected information on the proposed recipient, amount, communities to be served, and technology type for each rejected loan. Using this information, we analyzed the geographic distribution, including whether loans met various definitions of rural, and the repayment status of the loans.

To assess the relationship, if any, between RUS loans and broadband deployment and economic development in rural areas, we conducted statistical analyses and interviews. To assess broadband deployment, we used the most recent National Broadband Map's (NBM)[3] data on broadband availability to compare the number of providers in counties with approved RUS loan projects to counties with rejected RUS loan projects. NBM data currently available represent broadband availability as of June 2013. We also compared the number of broadband providers in select communities before and after the approval of a RUS loan; we selected these communities as part of our site visits, discussed below. For this analysis, we gathered information on broadband providers present in these communities before the RUS loan from the relevant loan files at USDA, and used NBM information to identify providers after the RUS loan approval.[4] To examine economic development in rural areas, we developed a regression model to assess the relationship between counties with approved loan projects and specific economic outcomes (i.e., number of business establishments, employment, and annual payroll). We assessed the reliability of RUS data by interviewing RUS officials about their databases and data collection practices. We also assessed the reliability of NBM data by reviewing how the map developers collect data and conduct quality assurance checks, as well as through interviews with stakeholders. Based on this information we determined that these data were sufficiently reliable for our reporting purposes. We also conducted site visits and phone interviews with stakeholders in seven states, which we selected to include communities with providers that have and have not received different kinds of RUS broadband loans.[5] As part of our site visits we interviewed, when possible, broadband providers, as well as state and local stakeholders such as Chambers of Commerce. We also examined prior academic studies of the RUS loan program as well as other research on the general impact of broadband availability and adoption on communities. We identified these studies through a literature search as well as interviews with stakeholders.

Finally, to determine the impact of reforms to the USF and ICC on the RUS broadband loan program, we reviewed relevant documentation, analyzed USF data, and conducted interviews. We reviewed FCC's 2011 USF/ICC Transformation Order that adopted changes to the USF and ICC, provided a framework for additional changes, and solicited comments regarding those changes.[6] We also reviewed public comments on the rulemakings proposed as part of this Transformation Order, as well as studies and reports that assess the impact of the reforms. To calculate the extent of USF support for RUS broadband borrowers, we examined data—for the years 2003 through 2013— reported in FCC's Universal Service Monitoring Report. We assessed the reliability of these data by reviewing relevant data collection and verification documents. Based on this information, we determined that the data provided to us were sufficiently reliable for our reporting purposes. Additionally, we conducted interviews with officials from RUS, FCC, a private bank (CoBank), and NTCA − The Rural Broadband Association. We also discussed these reforms with nine broadband providers that have and have not received USF support, as described above. Further details about our scope and methodology can be found in appendix I.

We conducted this performance audit from June 2013 to May 2014 in accordance with generally accepted government auditing standards. Those standards require that we plan and perform the audit to obtain sufficient, appropriate evidence to provide a reasonable basis for our findings and conclusions based on our audit objectives. We believe that the evidence obtained provides a reasonable basis for our findings and conclusions based on our audit objectives.

BACKGROUND

The provision of broadband Internet infrastructure and services in the United States is generally privately financed. Rural areas, though, can have conditions that increase the cost of broadband deployment, such as remote areas with challenging terrain like mountains, which increase construction costs, or conditions that make it difficult to recoup deployment costs, such as relatively low population densities and incomes.[7] These conditions make it less likely that a service provider will build out or maintain a network. Low population density can mean fewer potential subscribers, and lower-income populations are less likely to use broadband. There is also evidence that rural low-income households are less likely to use broadband than metropolitan low-income households.[8] As a result of these factors, rural areas tend to lag behind urban and suburban areas in broadband deployment.

However, because of broadband's economic and social benefits, several public programs aim to encourage greater investment in rural areas. RUS administers several such programs intended to accelerate the deployment of broadband services. One program is the Rural Broadband Access Loan and Loan Guarantee Program, which authorizes RUS to provide treasury rate loans, 4 percent loans, and loan guarantees.[9] The loan program was authorized by the Farm Security and Rural Investment Act of 2002 (2002 reauthorization act) and RUS approved the first loans under the program in fiscal year 2003.[10] On February 6, 2013, RUS published in the *Federal Register* the final rule implementing the loan program,[11] as reauthorized in 2008.[12] Entities eligible to receive these loans include corporations, limited liability companies, cooperative or mutual organizations, Indian tribes, and state or local governments.[13] The program is "technology neutral" in that RUS can finance any type of broadband service as long as the applicant plans to deliver broadband to every customer in the proposed service area at certain speeds.[14] The loan program was reauthorized by the 2014 reauthorization act, which modified some eligibility requirements and included a new requirement for any entity receiving a loan to submit a semiannual report, for the 3 years after completion of the project, which includes data on broadband adoption rates.[15] According to RUS officials we spoke with, until RUS publishes regulations implementing the changes in the 2014 reauthorization act, it will not accept new loan applications.[16] To administer the loan program, RUS has approximately 22 program staff as well as 25 field staff assisting part-time.

According to RUS rules for the loan program, the service area of a project eligible for RUS broadband financing must be entirely within a rural area, defined for this loan program as any area not contained in an incorporated city or town with a population in excess of 20,000 inhabitants, or an urbanized area contiguous and adjacent to a city or town that has a population greater than 50,000 inhabitants. In addition to being located within a rural area, a service area must meet the following conditions:

- At least 25 percent of the households are underserved, meaning they are offered broadband service by no more than one "incumbent service provider."[17] Incumbent service providers are broadband providers that RUS identifies as directly providing broadband service to at least 5 percent of the households within a service area.
- No part of the service area has three or more "incumbent service providers."
- No part of the funded service area overlaps the service area of current RUS borrowers and grantees.
- No part of the funded service area is included in a pending application before RUS seeking funding to provide broadband service.

RUS has a total authorized value of all the loans it can approve each fiscal year, based on lending authority approved in annual appropriations and the estimated long-term cost of extending credit over the life of the loans approved that fiscal year.[18] See table 1 below for yearly authorized total value of loans as well as loans approved.

RUS loans can have a variety of repayment outcomes. Loans are paid out as eligible project costs are incurred, on an agreed-upon repayment schedule. For the purposes of this report, "active" loans are those that are being paid back by the borrower as scheduled. "Repaid" loans include those that have already been fully paid back. When a loan is never paid out, it is referred to as a "rescission." Loans can also be reduced from the approved amount, for instance when a borrower does not need the remainder of a loan upon completion of a project. Borrowers can also fail to abide by the terms of the loans, such as missing payment deadlines, which may result in a "default."

Whereas RUS broadband loans are used as up-front capital to invest in broadband infrastructure, the USF has functioned as an ongoing subsidy for telecommunications providers that offer telephone and other communications services such as broadband access. The USF includes four programs that subsidize these providers.[19] Within the USF program, the largest amount of annual expenditures involve the High-Cost Program, which subsidizes telecommunications providers that serve rural, remote, and other areas where the costs of offering telephone service are high.[20] These subsidies allow providers to charge lower rates than otherwise would be feasible. This support has been a key revenue resource for some telecommunications providers that also offer broadband services, including RUS broadband borrowers.

FCC has adopted program rules that change USF support. These changes are outlined in an order released in November 2011, an order that FCC said "comprehensively reforms and modernizes" the universal service system to ensure that affordable voice and broadband service are available throughout the nation.[21] This USF/ICC Transformation Order requires that recipients of high-cost support offer voice and broadband as a condition for receiving USF support. FCC also reformed the ICC system. ICC is a system of payments between providers for the origination, transportation, and termination of telecommunications traffic. ICC payments have traditionally been governed by a complex but related system of federal and state rules than those governing universal service.

SINCE 2003, 100 LOANS HAVE BEEN MADE TO GEOGRAPHICALLY AND DEMOGRAPHICALLY DIVERSE AREAS, BUT OVER 40 PERCENT ARE NO LONGER ACTIVE

Communities Receiving RUS Loans Are Geographically and Demographically Diverse

RUS has approved 100 loans, out of 249 applications, through the Broadband Loan Program since 2003. The total dollar amount of the loans awarded to date is about $2 billion.[22] The agency has approved few loans since 2008, including none in fiscal year 2010. RUS officials stated that after the passage of the Recovery Act, RUS focused on administering the Broadband Initiatives Program.[23] Moreover, a lag occurred between the passage of the 2008 reauthorization act and completion of the regulations to carry out the law, in part because of RUS prioritized distribution of Recovery Act funding.

The geographic distribution of RUS loans is widespread, though with more loans going to providers serving the Great Plains, Midwestern and Southern states than to the east and west coasts. Providers in 43 states received one or more loans since 2002 (see figure 1).[24] The states where providers received the most loans include Iowa, Kansas, Minnesota, Oklahoma, and Texas. RUS officials stated that the loan program is intended to be geographically neutral, and they do not target particular regions of the country. As discussed further below, not all approved loans are still active. We did not observe significant geographic differences between loans with different repayment statuses.

Table 1. Rural Utilities Service (RUS) Rural Broadband Access Loan and Loan Guarantee Program, Value of Loans, Fiscal Years 2003-2013 (Dollar Figures in Millions)

Fiscal year	Total authorized value of loans	Loans approved[a]	Total value of loans made[b]
2003	$80	2	$56.26
2004	$602	33	$574.56
2005	$550	13	$111.42
2006	$500	15	$329.21
2007	$500	16	$250.96
2008	$300	13	$421.35[c]
2009	$400	4	$6.65
2010	$400	0	$0
2011	$400	1	$19.75
2012	$212	1	$68.9
2013	$42	2	$151.77[d]

Source: GAO summary of RUS data and appropriations acts.

[a] Some approved loans are no longer active, either because the borrower has defaulted on its loan payments or the loan was never paid out.

[b] These loan award totals include loans that were later reduced or rescinded. According to RUS officials, RUS did not utilize the entire total authorized amount of loans each year because in some years it lacked enough quality applications.

[c] Starting in 2005 Congress allowed RUS to carry over unobligated funds into the following fiscal year—initially for one year, and later, indefinitely. According to RUS, the value of loans approved in fiscal year 2008 includes loan amounts for which the subsidy cost was appropriated in fiscal year 2007 as well as in fiscal year 2008.

[d] The fiscal year 2013 award total is higher than the total authorized value of loans that year because a loan was approved and rescinded during this fiscal year, a situation that allowed RUS to award another loan in the same fiscal year.

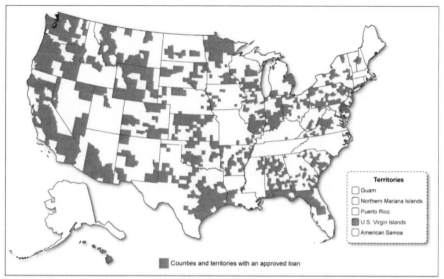

Source: GAO analysis of Rural Utilities Service data.
Note: For the purposes of this graphic, if a county had one or more communities served
    by an RUS loan, the entire county is deemed served. The highlighted areas
    therefore do not represent the exact service areas of all projects supported by the
    RUS broadband loan program.

Figure 1. U.S. Counties and Territories with One or More Approved RUS Broadband
Loans, 2002—2013.

RUS broadband borrowers are located in regions with varying topography,
including differing weather and terrain.[25] For example, we spoke to borrowers
in dissimilar regions, including North Dakota (plains with some hills); New
Mexico (high desert); and Vermont (rocky hills and mountains). Some aspects
of these rural areas can result in challenges for broadband deployment, with
some stakeholders stating that the unique characteristics of their region
affected the amount of time and resources they needed to install broadband.
Officials at a broadband provider we spoke with in New Mexico, for instance,
said that the extremely hard, rocky ground in the service area results in very
high per-mile costs for installing fiber infrastructure in the ground. Another
provider in North Dakota told us that the long winters limit the time available
for installing fiber to about 4 months a year.

    Loans have been made to providers in areas with a variety of
demographics and economies:

- On average, counties where RUS loans were approved have a higher poverty rate, 15.6 percent, than the national average, 14.9 percent. In these loan counties, the rate ranges from 4.2 percent to 41.1 percent, based on U.S. Census Bureau (Census) data.
- Overall, counties with approved RUS loans have a higher percentage of adults over age 65, 15.7 percent, than the national average, 13.2 percent. The range of this age group in loan counties is also large, from 4.1 to 44.5 percent.
- The per capita income of loan recipient communities is also diverse. For example, our site visit communities included Portales, New Mexico, with per capita income of $15,881, and Dickinson, North Dakota, with per capita income of $28,253.[26]
- Some areas where we conducted interviews, such as Eagle Butte, South Dakota, were highly rural and remote. These areas had low population densities and also tended to be lower-income, overall.
- Other site visit locations, including the rural communities of Hudson and Catskill, New York, were located in relative proximity to large cities, and had some of the characteristics of more urban areas, such as robust "creative economies." For example, Hudson, New York, is located within a 2 hour drive from both Albany and New York City, and has recently attracted a number of businesses such as art galleries.
- Two site visit communities, Dickinson, North Dakota, and Hobbs, New Mexico, have experienced recent surges in population and infrastructure needs associated with the oil and natural gas industry, according to providers with whom we spoke.

Communities Served by RUS Broadband Borrowers Generally Meet Past and Present Definitions of Rural

The definition of what constitutes a "rural" community can be difficult when determining how to target rural communities for broadband assistance. A narrower definition may mean that deserving communities are excluded. A broader definition, though, may mean that communities not traditionally considered "rural" or "underserved" may be eligible for financial assistance, which could then limit funds available to the most rural areas. The USDA's Office of Inspector General has reported that rural requirements are important to keep the focus of loans on rural areas that are unlikely to receive broadband service through the private market.[27]

When analyzed in the aggregate, the majority of active RUS loans since the program's inception satisfy RUS and other commonly accepted definitions of rural. The RUS definition of eligible rural areas for the loan program has been changed twice to better target loans to rural areas.[28] In 2008, for instance, the definition of an eligible community was changed to exclude communities adjacent to urbanized areas.[29] This change followed a 2005 finding by the USDA's Office of Inspector General that some loans had been made to areas that were not truly rural, such as suburban communities bordering large cities.[30] We found that the majority of active RUS loans were made to providers in communities that satisfy the 2008 and 2004 definitions of rural used by RUS.[31] Additionally, the majority of active loan communities meet alternative definitions of rural. Specifically, our analysis assessed whether loans could be considered rural using the standard Census definition as well as USDA's Rural-Urban Commuting Area Codes (RUCA). Census classifies a community as rural if it falls outside of an urban area, and most active loans adhered to this population density-based definition, whether 2000 or 2010 Census data were used.[32] The USDA Economic Research Service's 2013 RUCA is a more in-depth set of data that incorporate Census tract commuting patterns and other measures of "rurality" in addition to population density.[33] The majority of the active loans fell into the "large rural town" and "small town/isolated rural" categories.[34]

With only five loans approved since 2008, we were not able to assess whether the overall rurality of loans has changed as a result of the 2008 reauthorization act. Additionally, stakeholders generally did not object to the current definition of rural used by RUS. Some site-visit interviewees suggested that additional factors besides population, such as socioeconomic characteristics, be considered as part of the eligibility requirements.

Over 40 Percent of Approved Loans Are No Longer Active Because They Are in Default or Have Been Rescinded

Of the 100 RUS loans approved since 2002, 57 are active or have been repaid (see figure 2). The other 43 loans are no longer active, either because they have been rescinded or are in default. These inactive loans represent 43 percent of the total number of loans awarded and 54 percent of the total loan dollars awarded to date.

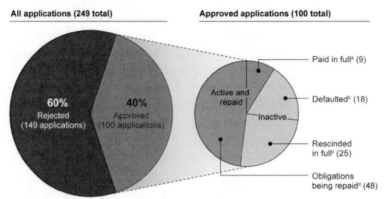

Source: GAO analysis of RUS data.

[a] Providers for these projects have paid back the entirety of their loans to RUS. We classify these as active for the purposes of this report.

[b] These projects have been unable to make payments as scheduled and are officially classified as in default by RUS.

[c] These loans have been effectively cancelled without any portion ever being advanced to the provider.

[d] These loans are in the process of being repaid.

Figure 2. Status of Broadband Loan-Program Applications, 2002—2013.

- The majority of RUS loans approved by RUS to date are *active* or have been repaid. These loans include 48 that are currently repaying outstanding obligations as scheduled, as well as 9 that have been fully paid back to the agency. Both of these categories include some loans that have been reduced, meaning the provider has elected to not accept the full loan amount or completed its project ahead of schedule and did not require the remaining funds.

- Twenty-five of the 100 loans approved to date have been *rescinded*, meaning that they were cancelled before any portion of the loan was paid out to the approved provider. RUS officials stated there are varying circumstances where a loan might be rescinded, including situations where the provider cannot meet equity requirements or the provider experiences significant financial problems before the principal has been loaned. Although providers sometimes voluntarily request a full rescission, that situation is less common.

- Eighteen loans approved to date are *in default*, a situation defined by RUS officials as when a borrower is unable to meet its payments over time and may require intervention by RUS and possibly the

Department of Justice to recover the funds that have been distributed.[35] Officials said loans generally default because the provider cannot produce the necessary revenue to support the broadband network and debt payments, often due to not attracting enough subscribers. When a provider misses a payment, RUS takes interim steps before classifying the loan as in default.[36] A defaulted loan may result in the cancellation of any unpaid portion of the loan.

- Throughout the time period of the loan program, RUS has rejected 149—60 percent—of the 249 applications received because providers did not meet the financial requirements for loans or proposed service areas did not meet the definition of rural, among other reasons, according to RUS officials. The primary reason for rejections is insufficient credit support to justify the project's "business case."

The USDA's Office of Inspector General noted in its 2005 review of the loan program that out of 28 approved pilot program loans, 6 were in default. Further, the Office of Inspector General said, "[H]ad the progress of these projects been timely and thoroughly monitored, RUS might have been able to avoid advancing loan funds to companies that were failing. Because these loans were not carefully serviced, these funds are not available to support future broadband loans."[37] Since the loan program was created in 2002, about 18 percent of all loans have defaulted.[38] In contrast, a private, but government-sponsored, lender that finances broadband projects we spoke with stated that only about 1 to 3 percent of its clients will fail to implement their projects. However, officials with that private lender noted that their investment strategy differs significantly from RUS, with RUS's program requirements allowing more risk in their loan portfolio. As RUS officials told us, private lenders can decline to award any loan, whereas RUS must implement the program in accordance with its authorizing statutes.

Loans that are approved by RUS require significant resources to review and monitor. According to RUS officials, these administrative costs are not just one-time expenses associated with the application review, but are incurred throughout the life of the loan.[39] For loans made to providers that experience financial challenges, RUS staff must conduct additional follow-up work, including work associated with any decisions to rescind a loan. Therefore, failure of many defaulted and fully rescinded projects to result in broadband service can represent an inefficient use of RUS resources. RUS acknowledged that dedicating resources to servicing loans in default takes away resources that could be used for evaluating new applications, but it did not agree that this is an inefficient use of resources. Additionally, the rescission of funding for projects in a year when RUS obligates the entirety of its total authorized value of loans that year could prevent more viable applicants from receiving loans.

Despite these issues, RUS has not gathered information or performed analysis to better understand what might lead a project to default or otherwise make a project a poor candidate for receiving the loan. According to RUS officials, a lack of staff resources has prevented them from studying the reasons for failed projects. Other USDA staff, though, such as researchers in the Economic Research Service who are responsible for informing and enhancing public and private decision making, may have the expertise to examine these issues. Additionally, RUS officials said the agency is undergoing a staff reorganization that will establish a branch to oversee loan performance.[40]

Federal guidance emphasizes the importance of assessing the risk associated with loan programs. Office of Management and Budget (OMB) guidance states that agencies should annually "take steps to evaluate and analyze existing asset portfolios" to identify ways to improve credit management and recoveries.[41] Also, as we have previously found, best practices for lenders emphasize an understanding of the risk posed by government loans, both on the level of individual loans and the overall portfolio.[42] To address credit risk, best-practice lenders focus on controlling the quality of individual loans approved. These efforts include routinely reviewing loan performance. By not identifying the common characteristics of defaulted and fully rescinded loans, if any, RUS may continue to expend resources on loans that ultimately do not succeed in providing funds to broadband providers for new or improved services.

RUS LOANS CAN HELP PROMOTE LIMITED BROADBAND DEPLOYMENT AND ECONOMIC DEVELOPMENT, BUT PERFORMANCE GOALS DO NOT FULLY ALIGN WITH PROGRAM'S PURPOSE

RUS Loans Can Help Overcome Financial Barriers to Deploying Broadband in Rural Areas

Broadband projects in rural areas are generally more expensive, on a cost-per-subscriber basis, than projects in metropolitan areas, creating a financial barrier to deployment, according to our review of the relevant literature. While the numbers of new broadband subscribers continue to grow overall, studies and data suggest that the broadband deployment rate in metropolitan areas is outpacing the deployment rate in rural areas.[43] The comparatively lower population density and income of rural areas are primary reasons why broadband is less deployed there than in suburban and urban areas. As a result, developing a business case to build broadband infrastructure that guarantees a return on investment can be difficult for rural providers. Aside from RUS loans, there are few alternatives for financing rural broadband projects because banks typically do not make loans for projects that lack a strong business case.

According to several stakeholders we spoke with, RUS loans have helped providers overcome financial barriers to broadband deployment, allowing providers to upgrade existing service to faster technologies and expand deployment to new subscribers in rural areas. In these areas, RUS loans can be an essential source of financing. Officials we spoke with in four rural communities said that broadband services would likely not exist in very rural areas without federal support. For example, representatives of providers in Kansas and Vermont told us their RUS loan was essential to construction of broadband infrastructure in their rural service areas.

According to our analysis of affected areas, the RUS loan program has had a mixed record of increasing overall broadband deployment. In order to further assess the impact of loans on broadband deployment, we compared the number of broadband providers in counties that have RUS-financed broadband projects to the number of providers in counties that applied but were rejected for a RUS loan as well as counties that had fully rescinded loans, using the latest data from the NBM. Our goal with this analysis was to compare counties that were generally similar but for the presence of a RUS loan. Overall, counties with RUS-financed projects generally do not have more broadband providers than similar counties. Specifically, as of June 2013, counties with RUS projects had an average of 4.9 broadband providers, whereas counties with rejected and rescinded projects had an average of 5.1 broadband providers.[44] While this analysis suggests that RUS loans have little to no overall impact on the number of broadband providers, the county-level data could mask local impacts of loans. Indeed, information we collected during our site visits indicate that RUS loans can lead to enhanced broadband deployment in specific rural areas within counties. For example, rural areas around East Corinth, Vermont, had no broadband access until the local provider was awarded a RUS loan. Catskill, New York, only had one broadband provider until a RUS loan enabled another provider to build into the community. A RUS loan also helped a provider upgrade service in rural areas around Eagle Butte, South Dakota, from dial-up access to digital subscriber line service. In a February 2014 report, we also found that providers have used federal programs to expand their existing networks by laying new fiber optic lines or using other technologies to make broadband available in areas that were previously unserved or underserved.[45]

Some rural areas do not have enough potential subscribers to justify the upgrade or expansion of broadband services even with a RUS loan. One provider noted that even with a federal grant—which would not require repayment—extending service to some rural geographies or upgrading services to state-of-the-art technology could be prohibitively expensive over the long-term since the ongoing costs of providing service can be higher than the revenue generated by the rural subscribers.

RUS Loans Can Create Opportunities for Modest Economic Development and Enhance the Quality of Life in Rural Areas

Economic Development

Several stakeholders told us that broadband services financed with RUS loans help local businesses be more competitive, fostering economic development. Having the ability to communicate and conduct business online reduces the effect of physical distances that are otherwise a barrier. According to state officials in South Dakota, broadband access gives rural businesses the opportunity to participate in the wider national economy and potentially the global economy. They noted that with broadband, ranchers have access to a larger market because they can participate in online auctions and show cattle to potential buyers via streaming video. Rural development officials in Vermont also told us that broadband enables online financial transactions for rural residents to conduct both bookkeeping and shopping, provides a forum for community outreach, and facilitates increased tourism, among other things. According to one official we spoke with in Vermont, some tourists prefer to have broadband access while vacationing.

Businesses and entrepreneurs may choose to locate in a community in part based on access to broadband. According to two business site selection experts–consultants who specialize in helping businesses identify new business locations–we spoke with, reliable broadband networks are now critical for rural businesses. The lack of broadband connectivity in a rural area could significantly hinder the ability of that area to attract and retain businesses. These perspectives are consistent with broader academic research, which has found that access to reliable and affordable broadband is viewed as particularly important for the economic development of rural areas because it enables individuals and businesses to participate fully in the online economy regardless of geographical location.

Since a variety of factors can influence local economic development, we developed a model to assess the impact of the RUS loan program on economic development. We used a regression model since this technique can help control for a variety of extraneous factors, such as growth of the national economy in general. Specifically, our model compared employment, payroll, and business establishments of counties affected by RUS loans to similarly rural counties that were not affected by loans, using RUS and Census data from 2003 through 2011.[46]

According to our analysis of RUS loans and economic development data, counties affected by at least one approved RUS loan were associated with modestly higher levels of employment and payroll after the year of loan approval and in all subsequent years, as compared to counties that did not receive RUS loans.[47] We found that RUS loans are associated with a one to four percent higher level of employment and payroll in affected counties. As noted above, stakeholders told us that broadband access can help make businesses more efficient, which can lead to job creation and increased payroll. However, we found no relationship between RUS loans and the number of total business establishments in a community. We ran the model using several specifications, most of which involved alternative comparison groups of unaffected counties, and our results were consistent.

Several factors could contribute to the findings from our model. The lack of effect on the number of establishments, and the modest impact on employment and payroll, may be the result of the county being too coarse a level of analysis for evidence of impact to emerge, meaning the county's scale overwhelms in size the service area of broadband providers receiving loans. Additionally, the effect of the loan program may not be strong enough to affect the number of business establishments at the county level. While e-commerce is greatly facilitated by broadband access, it can hinder rural businesses by making it cheaper and easier for local residents to shop on-line rather than at local establishments. Nevertheless, our results are broadly consistent with information we gathered in site-visit interviews about how enhanced broadband access enabled by the RUS loan program can have a modest, positive impact on the local economy. As an official at the Chamber of Commerce in Columbia, New York, noted, lack of broadband access outside of major towns is hindering growth, and investment in broadband infrastructure would accelerate economic activity in Columbia County.

Quality of Life

Beyond economic development, broadband services financed with RUS loans can enhance the quality of life in rural communities. For example, broadband can bring educational opportunities to rural communities through online-learning technologies. Two South Dakota college officials we spoke with said broadband services have enabled their students to access on-line journals through the local university. Video teleconferencing enables students at several schools to attend the classes of a single instructor. Earning course credits online can also be less expensive than taking classes in person, helping students save money and expanding access to education to lower-income students. Telemedicine and telehealth[48] have been hailed as vital to health care in rural communities, by expanding the medical services available. According to a provider we spoke with, RUS-financed broadband services in rural South Dakota have facilitated the remote use of some Veterans Affairs services. A provider in Kansas said hospitals in rural areas also rely on telemedicine technology to access information and personnel at larger medical institutions.

Broadband can also create opportunities to search for jobs and work from home. Access that allows individuals to work from home ("telework") can enhance businesses and organizations' continuity of operations, provide new job opportunities to retirees and the disabled, among others, and can benefit the environment. According to officials in the Catskills area of New York, weekend residents would spend more time in their second homes there if they could telework, which could bring greater revenues to local merchants and restaurants. Officials with a rural South Dakota broadband provider noted that more people are working from home, as evidenced by the amount of bandwidth being used. Broadband can also facilitate online job searching. South Dakota state officials also cited a state workforce-development program, Dakota Roots, which works to "re-stake" former South Dakota residents who would like to return to South Dakota by connecting them with employment opportunities posted at their website.

USDA Annual Performance Goals and Measures Do Not Fully Align with the Loan Program's Purpose

USDA's *Annual Performance Report* (*APR*) provides information on the achievements of USDA's programs each fiscal year. The *APR* is produced in part to satisfy requirements in the GPRA Modernization Act of 2010[49] (that updated the Government Performance and Results Act of 1993[50]) which along with OMB requirements[51] aims to ensure agencies use performance information in decision making and hold them accountable for achieving results and improving government performance. As our past work has shown, an attribute of a successful performance measure is whether it aligns with division and agency-wide goals.[52] We have also found that congressional staff wants a clear depiction at the program level of the linkages between program resources, strategies, and the objectives they aim to achieve.[53]

The goals in USDA's *APR* do not fully align to the purpose of the RUS broadband loan program. The purposes of the loan program are to improve broadband deployment in rural areas—that is, increase the number of broadband subscribers with access to new or improved broadband service—and ultimately increase economic opportunity in rural America. USDA's fiscal year 2013 *APR* includes a strategic objective to "enhance rural prosperity," under which is an annual performance goal related to broadband adoption and the broadband loan program: "number of borrowers/subscribers receiving new or improved telecommunications services." This performance goal is assessed using data on the number of subscribers to be served for each loan, derived from applicants' estimates in their approved loan applications.[54] This method does not measure actual adoption of RUS-financed broadband services. As the National Broadband Plan states, "adoption is necessary for utilization, but utilization is necessary to extract value from a [broadband] connection."[55] Furthermore, USDA's *APR* does not have any goals or measures to determine the loan program's progress towards economic development outcomes.

As our past work has shown, agency performance goals that do not link to program goals can lead to incentives and behaviors that do not support the achievement of division or agency-wide goals.[56] As agencies develop annual performance goals as envisioned by the GPRA Modernization Act, they can serve as a bridge that links long-term goals to agencies' daily operations. For example, an annual goal that is linked to a program and also to a long-term goal can be used both to hold agencies and program offices accountable for achieving those goals and to assess the reasonableness and appropriateness of those goals for the agency as a whole. Ensuring the linkage between the loan program's purpose and the annual performance goals may be especially important since, as we discuss above, the RUS loan program has had mixed results with respect to improving broadband deployment and economic development. Performance goals that better evaluate progress toward the loan program's goals may help USDA and Congress better monitor the outcomes of the loan program.

FCC REFORMS OF USF AND ICC HAVE CREATED TEMPORARY UNCERTAINTY THAT MAY BE HINDERING INVESTMENT IN BROADBAND

About Half of RUS Broadband Borrowers with Active Loans Have Received USF Support, and Most Received ICC Support

About half of active RUS broadband borrowers have received USF support, which serves as an ongoing subsidy for telecommunications providers. Indeed, some investments by RUS borrowers have been made with the assumption on their part that at least some revenue to repay the loans would come from the USF. Fifty-one percent of RUS broadband borrowers with active loans—that is, loans that have not defaulted or been rescinded in full—received support from the USF High-Cost Program since 2003 (25 out of 49 borrowers; some of these borrowers received multiple loans). About 35 percent of all RUS broadband borrowers—that is, all providers with an approved loan regardless of loan status—have received USF support (30 out of 86 borrowers; some of these borrowers received multiple loans).[57] In addition to the RUS broadband borrowers that received direct USF support, 10 borrowers that do not receive direct support have a parent company that has received support.

The level of USF support for RUS broadband borrowers, overall, grew from 2003 to 2012. The average amount of USF support for all 30 RUS broadband borrowers that have received support was $2,067,328, per year, from 2003 to 2013.[58] During this time period, the year with the highest average amount of USF support for all RUS broadband borrowers was 2012, while the lowest was 2003. The support for active RUS broadband borrowers specifically has ranged from $8,162,834 in 2012 for Paul Bunyan Rural

Telephone Cooperative in Minnesota, to $39 in 2007 for SS Telecom, Inc. in South Dakota.[59]

According to a RUS official, most broadband borrowers make and receive ICC payments—as part of the system of payments between providers for telecommunications traffic—since most borrowers offer both broadband and traditional telephone service. However, data on the total amount of ICC paid and received by individual providers are not available.

Reforms May Change Amount of USF and ICC Support for RUS Broadband Borrowers

Reforms begun under the 2011 USF/ICC Transformation Order may change the amount of USF support for the majority of RUS broadband borrowers that receive support. In particular, with the Transformation Order, FCC took a number of actions:

- froze certain USF support for certain providers at 2011 levels;[60]
- capped total per-line support as well as capital and operating expenses;[61]
- eliminated or began phasing down certain types of support;[62] and
- created the Connect America Fund (CAF), which will ultimately replace the high-cost fund for certain providers.[63]

However, many of the changes to the USF High-Cost Program that will affect RUS broadband borrowers have not yet been implemented. In the Transformation Order, FCC proposed changes to its methods for distributing funds to address some of the recognized program inefficiencies, but many of the details and mechanics of the transition from legacy high-cost support to the CAF have not yet been determined. In the meantime, RUS broadband borrowers—which are generally smaller providers operating solely in rural areas—will continue to receive support, with some modifications, from current support mechanisms pending full transition to the CAF or a similar mechanism tailored to small rural providers. Details of how future support will be determined are pending the completion of an extensive Further Notice of Proposed Rulemaking issued with the Transformation Order.[64]

In the USF/ICC Transformation Order, FCC also reformed the ICC system. The current system involves payments—governed by various state and federal rules—between providers for telecommunications traffic. In the

Transformation Order, FCC adopted a uniform national "bill-and-keep" framework as the ultimate end state for all telecommunications traffic exchanged with a local carrier.[65] According to FCC, under this approach, carriers look first to their subscribers to cover the costs of the network, then to explicit universal service support where necessary. Because this is a default methodology, carriers remain free to negotiate alternative arrangements that include carrier payments. As a result of the USF/ICC Transformation Order, all terminating access rates (generally governing charges for calls that begin and end in different local calling areas) and reciprocal compensation rates (generally for calls within the same area) were capped as of December 29, 2011. Over time (9 years for small, rural providers), certain terminating access rates and all reciprocal compensation rates will gradually be phased out. FCC has sought further comment on the proper transition and recovery mechanism for the remaining ICC rates.

Uncertain Levels of Future Support Hinder Broadband Investment, According to Stakeholders

With the elimination of some USF support and other changes implemented to date, a majority of RUS broadband borrowers have seen reductions in the amount of USF revenue they receive. Specifically, 18 of the 30 RUS borrowers directly receiving high-cost support in 2011 received less support in 2013 than in 2011. These 18 borrowers lost an average of 31 percent of their USF support over those 2 years, though not all of that loss can be directly attributed to USF reforms.[66]

Some RUS broadband borrowers may have also seen net reductions in ICC support. According to an industry association we spoke with, small, rural providers like most RUS borrowers are generally net recipients of ICC, paying out less than they receive. The incremental decreases in ICC rates implemented to date may have therefore resulted in net revenue reductions for these small, rural providers.[67] FCC is implementing a "transitional recovery mechanism" to facilitate providers' gradual transition away from ICC revenues reduced as part of the Transformation Order.[68] This mechanism allows providers to recover a portion of lost ICC revenues from increases in end-user (e.g., consumer) rates and, where appropriate, universal service support through ICC CAF.

Despite concerns, reductions in USF support have not limited the ability of broadband borrowers to pay back RUS loans, to date. According to RUS officials, the agency evaluates loan applicants' ability to pay back a loan based on their overall financial situation, including any support they expect to receive from the USF and ICC. RUS does not consider whether the parent company of the applicant receives such support. Some RUS loans were approved, and investments made by borrowers who assumed that at least some revenue to repay the loans would come from the USF. As the RUS Administrator noted in a 2012 letter to FCC, "changes to the federal USF and ICC can have a direct impact on the ability of existing RUS farm bill [broadband] borrowers to repay their outstanding loans and complete the construction of wireline broadband systems."[69] Additionally, according to RUS officials as well as a RUS broadband borrower we spoke with, reduced support for parent companies can have an indirect impact on borrowers, such as a decrease in the parent company's investment in the subsidiary. Nevertheless, FCC maintained in the Transformation Order that USF reforms "will in general not materially impact the ability of these carriers to service their existing debt." To date, no RUS broadband borrower that received USF support has defaulted on its loan. In contrast, as noted above, 18 other RUS loan program loans have defaulted.

Uncertainty regarding future support has led to some RUS broadband borrowers limiting broadband infrastructure investment. As noted above, some important details of the reforms to USF high-cost support have not been determined. Some broadband providers that we spoke with, including those that have and have not received a RUS loan, noted that they have postponed infrastructure investments pending these USF reforms. One provider in rural New Mexico we spoke with said that it is hesitant to build additional broadband infrastructure, especially high-cost fiber to the home, because it fears the consequences of USF reforms. Another provider in South Dakota maintained that it is not borrowing any more money for broadband build out because it does not know how much USF revenue to expect in the future. According to a study by a law firm of USF reforms, "since telecom services require high upfront capital investments that are recovered over a number of years, there will be lesser and more sporadic investment in high-cost areas, due to the lower levels of support funding and increased uncertainty."[70] According to officials we spoke with at CoBank, a government-sponsored bank that supports agriculture and the rural economy, the "bottom line" impact of USF reforms is that small, rural providers will likely have reduced access to debt capital, restricting their ability to upgrade or expand broadband networks. With broadband providers hesitant to invest in infrastructure projects, demand has decreased for the RUS loan program. For instance, RUS received 29 applications for loans in fiscal years 2011—2013, compared to 130 in the first 3 full years of the program.[71] Nevertheless, FCC recently reported that since adoption of the Transformation Order the number of Census blocks with broadband service of at least 3 megabits per second download speed has increased.[72] In addition, on April 23, 2014, the FCC issued a news release stating that it had adopted an order that will eliminate a rule that may have unintentionally encouraged providers to limit their investment in broadband-capable networks.[73]

Much of the uncertainty regarding future USF support will be resolved with the full implementation of the USF/ICC Transformation Order, but the complexity of the reforms may result in a long implementation period. The rulemaking process being conducted to determine the mechanisms for future USF support requires FCC to provide the public with notice of its proposed and final rules, and with an opportunity to comment as the rules are developed. FCC officials told us that the rulemakings associated with the Transformation Order have been numerous and complex, and that the current Chairman has remained open to modifying proposed rules based on stakeholder feedback. As we have previously found, the complexity and number of rulemakings within a docket and the priority FCC places on a rulemaking contribute to the length of time dockets and rulemakings remaining open.[74] Moreover, elements of the USF/ICC Transformation Order have been appealed.[75]

CONCLUSION

Broadband is now recognized as a necessity for economic and social life in America, and several public programs aim to encourage greater investment in rural areas. USDA's RUS is charged with administering one of these programs, which provides low-cost loans to rural communities, but the program has experienced mixed results. For instance, over 40 percent of approved loans are no longer active, with many having not resulted in new or improved broadband services. Considerable resources are invested by RUS to administer these loans and their failures therefore may represent an inefficient use of RUS resources. Studying the characteristics of rescinded and defaulted loans could enable USDA to better recognize loan applications that may not result in successful projects and therefore better target its limited resources.

Even RUS loans that do not default or are rescinded may not significantly increase broadband deployment or economic development in rural areas. Based on our analysis, we found that RUS loans help promote modest broadband deployment and economic development in affected rural areas. USDA evaluates progress toward these and other outcomes in its *APR*, though the performance goals it uses do not fully align with the purpose of the RUS broadband loan program. Given the modest impact of the loan program, aligning its performance goals with the program's purpose could help RUS better evaluate the loan program's performance and provide Congress with more information on the outcomes of the program so it can better hold USDA accountable for achieving results and improving government performance.

RECOMMENDATIONS

We recommend the Secretary of Agriculture take the following two actions:

- evaluate loans made by RUS through the broadband loan program to identify characteristics of loans that may be at risk of rescission or default; and
- align performance goals under the "enhance rural prosperity" strategic objective in the *APR* to the broadband loan program's purpose, to the extent feasible.

AGENCY COMMENTS AND OUR EVALUATION

We provided a draft of this report to FCC for review and comment. FCC provided comments in a letter from the Chief, Wireline Competition Bureau. In its letter, FCC neither agreed nor disagreed with the report's findings. FCC provided comments on the presentation of certain facts related to USF programs. FCC said that although our report finds that uncertainty about the amount of high-cost support RUS borrowers would receive under FCC's reformed universal service program has negatively affected investment in broadband, FCC recently adopted an Order eliminating a rule that may have unintentionally encouraged carriers to limit their investment in broadband networks. We added text to our report about this Order. Additionally, FCC noted the adoption of a mechanism to mitigate the impact of reduced ICC on providers. We moved our text discussing this mechanism from a footnote to the body of the report and also noted that FCC's USF/ICC Transformation Order was never intended to be revenue-neutral for providers.

We also provided a draft of this report to USDA for review and comment. In an email received on May 9, 2014, a Management Analyst with USDA on behalf of the Assistant Administrator, Telecommunications Program, stated that RUS generally agreed with the facts presented in the report and will strive to fully implement our recommendations. However, RUS commented on the presentation of six facts in the report.

First, RUS said that it did not agree with our presentation of a map of areas served by RUS broadband loans (figure 1). RUS's comments indicated that the map may overstate the extent of loan service areas. However, the intent of this map is not to illustrate the extent of loan service areas but rather to illustrate the geographic distribution of RUS loans; the title and legend for the map clearly note that it reflects counties and territories with one or more approved RUS loans and we include a note explaining our methodology below the map. Thus, we continue to believe that its presentation is appropriate for the purpose intended.

Second, RUS noted that the areas around Catskill and Hudson, New York, which we describe as being relatively close to large metropolitan areas, qualified for financing according to the statutory requirements of the program; RUS also said that because an area is close to an urban area does not mean it is an urban area. We did not assess whether the service areas of loan projects complied with statutory requirements, though based on our site visits, we agree that the areas around Catskill and Hudson are rural, and revised the report to clarify this point.

Third, RUS noted that it disagreed with the 2005 USDA Office of Inspector General finding about the pilot loan program that our report discusses; RUS said that it did monitor projects, and that the purpose of a pilot program is to try different approaches, which inherently involves taking on additional risk to determine the best approach. While we found the Office of Inspector General's findings sufficiently reliable for our purposes, we added text to our report indicating that RUS disagreed with the Inspector General's findings and continues to do so.

Fourth, RUS said that our comparison of the RUS loan default rate to a private lender may give the wrong impression, since RUS takes on more risk than a private lender and thus may have more defaults. We acknowledge that RUS takes on more risks than private lenders and may therefore have a higher default rate. However, even considering the additional requirements and risk inherent in the RUS loan program, its default rate is six times higher than the private lender with whom we spoke and we believe this warrants further examination by USDA. As we recommend above, we believe USDA should evaluate loans made by RUS through the broadband loan program to identify characteristics of loans that may be at risk of rescission or default.

Fifth, RUS agreed that dedicating resources to servicing loans in default takes away resources that could be used for evaluating new applications, but RUS does not consider this an inefficient use of resources as stated in our report; rather, RUS said that additional resources would allow it to be more effective in making funds available to rural areas for broadband service. We added text to the report further explaining RUS's view on this issue; however, we continue to believe, as we recommend, that a better understanding of the characteristics of loans that may be at risk of rescission or default would help RUS use its resources more effectively.

Finally, RUS noted two concerns with our analysis of the number of broadband providers in counties with and without RUS loans. First, RUS said it is unfair to compare the number of providers in a county in 2013 when loans to that county may have been approved as far back as 2003. Second, RUS said that our analysis misrepresents the impact of RUS loans on broadband deployment because it assumes the entire county is served when only a small portion of a county may have actually received funds for broadband. One of the goals of the RUS loan program is to promote broadband service in communities where it would not otherwise exist. Accordingly, we assessed the extent to which the number of broadband providers in communities that received loans differed from communities that did not receive loans. The timing of the loan—whether it was made in 2003 or 2011, for instance—is not relevant to this analysis, since we were focused on the current state of broadband service. Comparing the current state of broadband service in areas that did and did not receive loans helps demonstrate the extent to which the loan program may be increasing the number of broadband providers. The fact that our analysis also uses counties, rather than individual communities, is also not a significant limitation because the data should show the presence of additional broadband service as a result of the loans even if the loans only affect portions of those counties. Therefore, we believe that this analysis is appropriate as one source of evidence about the impact of the RUS loan program on broadband deployment.

Mark Goldstein
Director, Physical Infrastructure Issues

APPENDIX I. SCOPE AND METHODOLOGY

To examine the geographic distribution and financial performance of loans, we gathered and analyzed Rural Utilities Service (RUS) loan data from 2003—2013. Specifically, we collected information on the recipient, approval date, amount, repayment status, as well as the proposed technology and communities to be served by the project for each loan approved by RUS as part of the Rural Broadband Access Loan and Loan Guarantee Program ("loan program"), including loans that have been rescinded. We also collected information on the proposed recipient, amount, communities to be served, and technology type for each rejected loan. Using this information, we assessed the distribution of active, rescinded, and rejected loans by state and region. We also analyzed the extent to which the loans met various definitions of rural, including those adopted by RUS for the loan program in 2002, 2004, and 2008, as well as the U.S. Census Bureau (Census) definition (areas not within urbanized areas) and the U.S. Department of Agriculture's (USDA) Rural-Urban Commuting Area (RUCA) Census tract-based codes. We selected these definitions of "rural" based on discussions with stakeholders and studies of defining rural.[76] We determined whether loans met these definitions of rural by examining the extent to which the proposed communities to be served by the loan project together satisfied by the definition of rural.[77] Finally, we used the RUS information to summarize the repayment status of loans, including the number and type of active, defaulted, and rescinded loans.

To assess the relationship, if any, between RUS loans and broadband deployment in rural areas, we conducted statistical analysis using National Broadband Map data on broadband availability, comparing counties with approved RUS loan projects to counties with rejected and fully rescinded RUS loan projects. Specifically, we identified counties with approved RUS loan projects as well as those with rejected and fully rescinded projects from the RUS loan information noted above.[78] For counties that had both approved and rejected loan projects, we treated it as an approved loan county, since it has been "treated" by the RUS loan program through its approved loan. Rejected and rescinded loan project counties therefore included only those counties with rejected and/or fully rescinded loans. We identified the current number of broadband providers in those counties using National Broadband Map data downloaded from the website created and maintained by the National Telecommunications and Information Administration, in collaboration with the Federal Communications Commission (FCC). We used the most recent data available, which were current as of June 2013. In addition to the analysis comparing areas with approved, rejected, and fully rescinded loans, we also examined the broadband providers in select communities before and after the approval of a RUS loan. We selected these communities as part of our site visits, discussed below. We gathered the information on broadband providers present in these communities before the RUS loan from the relevant RUS loan files at USDA. We again used the National Broadband Map information to identify the providers present in these communities after the RUS loan approval. Few loans have been approved since 2008, so we determined that sufficient time had passed for most projects financed with RUS loans to have been substantially completed.

To assess the relationship, if any, between RUS loans and economic development in rural areas, we conducted statistical analysis of RUS and Census data. We developed a regression model using a panel dataset to assess the relationship between counties with approved loan projects and specific economic outcomes (number of business establishments, employment, and annual payroll).[79] For more information on this model, see appendix II.

We assessed the reliability of RUS data by interviewing RUS officials about their databases and data collection practices. We also assessed the reliability of National Broadband Map data by reviewing its data collection procedures and methods, including how the map developers collect data and conduct quality assurance checks, as well as through interviews with stakeholders.[80] We also assessed the reliability of Census data by reviewing its data collection procedures and methods. Based on this information we determined that the data provided to us were sufficiently reliable for our reporting purposes.

We also examined prior academic studies and government reports. As background, we reviewed relevant USDA Office of Inspector General reports. Additionally, to inform our quantitative analysis and provide additional information on the relationship between broadband and economic development, we examined prior academic studies of the RUS loan program as well as government and academic research on the general impact of broadband availability and adoption on communities. We identified these studies through a literature search of the ArticleFirst, Engineering Information Compendex, Inside Conferences, NTIS, PAIS International, PapersFirst, ProQuest, SciSearch, Social SciSearch, and WorldCat databases, as well as interviews with stakeholders. At least two GAO analysts reviewed the studies and reports we cite in this report for methodological adequacy.

For additional information on the relationships, if any, between RUS loans and broadband deployment and economic development, we conducted site visits to 16 communities in rural areas. These areas were selected to include providers who did and did not receive RUS loans as well as stakeholders in surrounding communities and state capitals. We also identified communities and RUS broadband loans with varying experiences and perspectives. The specific criteria used to identify site-visit locations included the status of the loan (if relevant), the size of the loan, location, technology of loan project (if relevant), and date of loan approval (if relevant). Based on these criteria, we conducted physical visits to North and South Dakota as well as New York and Vermont. These site visits included loan service areas (consisting of one or more communities) in a variety of regions, with active, rescinded, and rejected loans. They also included four loan service areas with loans above the median loan size and five loan service areas below median loan size ($8,249,250). They also included a loan service area with one of the four loans approved after 2008, as well as loan projects utilizing three different technology types. Although using these criteria allowed us, in our view, to obtain information from a diverse mix of RUS broadband borrowers, the findings from our site visits cannot be generalized to all borrowers because they were selected as part of a nonprobability sample.

As part of our site visits, we interviewed, when possible, local broadband providers, including any that have applied for and received RUS loans. We also interviewed staff and members of local Chambers of Commerce, state and local government officials involved in broadband policy, and staff at state and local advocacy and economic development organizations. For additional information, we also interviewed broadband providers in Kansas, Louisiana, and New Mexico separate from our in-person site visits. In total, we spoke with broadband providers that have been approved for 10 of the 100 loans to date.

To determine the impact of reforms to the Universal Service Fund (USF) High-Cost program and Intercarrier Compensation (ICC) on the RUS broadband loan program, we reviewed FCC's 2011 USF/ICC Transformation Order that proposed changes to the USF and ICC mechanisms for determining support.[81] We also reviewed stakeholder submissions to the rulemakings proposed as part of this Transformation Order, as well as studies and reports that assess the impact of the reforms. To calculate the extent of USF support for RUS broadband borrowers, we examined data—for the years 2003 through 2013— reported in FCC's Universal Service Monitoring Report. We assessed the reliability of this data by reviewing relevant data collection and verification documents. Based on this information, we determined that the data provided to us were sufficiently reliable for our reporting purposes.

To better understand the impact of these reforms on RUS broadband borrowers, we also conducted interviews with officials from RUS, FCC, CoBank, and NTCA–The Rural Broadband Association. We also discussed these reforms with broadband providers that have and have not received USF support, as described above.

We conducted this performance audit from June 2013 to May 2014 in accordance with generally accepted government auditing standards. Those standards require that we plan and perform the audit to obtain sufficient, appropriate evidence to provide a reasonable basis for our findings and conclusions based on our audit objectives. We believe that the evidence obtained provides a reasonable basis for our findings and conclusions based on our audit objectives.

APPENDIX II. ECONOMIC DEVELOPMENT MODEL METHODOLOGY AND RESULTS

This appendix discusses the methodology used to develop a model analyzing the relationship between the RUS broadband loan program and economic activity in rural areas. In this appendix, we provide information on the scope, data, model, and results of our analysis.

Scope and Data

The time frame for our analysis was 2003 through 2011 because those are the years for which RUS and relevant Census data are available. The RUS broadband loan program was authorized in 2002 to finance the construction of broadband infrastructure in rural areas, following an earlier pilot program.[82] The first loans, though, were approved in 2003, so the relevant information associated with RUS loans begins in 2003. Broadband infrastructure projects funded by the RUS broadband loan program vary in geographic size. Projects must be designed to serve rural communities, although the geographic footprints of the proposed rural broadband projects do not consistently correspond to geographic units for which relevant data are collected. Some projects span more than one county, while others are focused on a specific area within a single county. We chose to focus our analysis at the county level, because counties, more fully (although still incompletely) than zip codes or

Census tracts, encompass the geographical extent of local markets. Though the most recent loan was approved in 2013, the relevant annual county-level Census data on economic activity are only available through 2011.

To conduct our analysis, we acquired data from RUS on all applications for RUS loans. Some of these applications were approved while others were rejected by RUS. The data we received from RUS included the list of communities (i.e., cities, towns, and Census Designated Places) to be served by each loan project. For those projects that were approved, we also received data on the approval date and the loan's current repayment status. By matching the list of communities to Census data, we identified the counties associated with each project. This information allowed us to categorize each county as part of the service area of an approved project, a rejected project, a project for which loan funds had been rescinded by RUS, or not part of any project service area. Some counties included the service areas of more than one approved project; others included the service areas of, for instance, both approved and rejected projects. For the purposes of this analysis, we classified every county associated with an approved project that has not been rescinded as being in *active* status, regardless of whether that county included the service area of a rescinded or rejected project. Counties associated with loans that have been rescinded were classified as being in *rescinded* status. Counties associated with rejected loans were classified as *rejected*.

We also acquired data from the Census. Specifically, we used County Business Pattern data on county employment, annual payroll, and number of business establishments from 2003 through 2011. Economic development has no universal definition or measure, but can be assessed using a variety of proxy measures. We identified our three measures of economic activity because they have been used in the past to assess the effect of a federal program on economic development. Specifically, in a 2006 report assessing the impact of Empowerment Zones on economic development, we used Census data on unemployment rates and the number of business establishments.[83] Additionally, in their analysis of the RUS loan program, Kandilov and Renkow used Census data on the number of business establishments, employment, and annual payroll as measures of economic development.[84] Further, other studies have examined the impact of broadband availability and adoption on economic outcomes, using variables such as unemployment, household income, and number of firms or establishments.[85]

Because the RUS program targets communities in rural areas, we wanted to restrict our analysis to rural counties and to examine whether our results were sensitive to the characterization of rural used to select counties. We used two county-level data sources to define rural areas at the county level. We used Census information on county rural and urban population characteristics as of 2010. As an alternative, we also used USDA data that placed each county into one of nine categories on a rural–urban continuum.

Additionally, as part of the proximity-scoring process, to be discussed in more detail below, we used additional County Business Patterns data for an earlier time period and 2000 Census information on demographic characteristics of counties. Finally, we used the Gross Domestic Product price index to express payroll dollars in terms of calendar year 2013 values.

Model

Structure

Many factors affect changes in economic activity. In any particular place, economic activity can be influenced by natural resources in that area and the current fortunes of whatever industries have located there historically, among other factors. In any particular time, regional or national economies may be growing rapidly or may be in recession. In addition, the degree to which any area is connected to the broader economy has implications for economic performance. In this regard, the quality of access to transportation networks has long been identified as among the important factors explaining economic development. More recently, access to broadband infrastructure has been thought of in this context, and particularly in the case of rural communities, real and perceived lack of broadband access has been thought to hinder economic development and has provided the motivation for the RUS broadband loan program, among others.

Given that broadband infrastructure is one of many factors that could be associated with economic activity, it may be difficult in a modeling context to assemble all of the factors that may be necessary to distinguish one county from another in terms of its resources, industrial structure, and labor force characteristics, among other things. One estimation technique that can be useful in this kind of situation is to take advantage of the panel characteristics of this data. A panel data set is one in which there are observations for a given set of cross-section units, in this case county-level measures of economic activity, over several time periods, in this case years. A fixed-effects model of panel data can have two sets of dummy variables, one for each cross-section unit and one set for each time period. In our model, the former account for those observed and unobserved effects that are constant over time but affect economic activity in a particular county, and the latter for effects that are constant across counties but vary over time, such as the condition of the national economy. The variable in which we are interested is defined as a zero (0) or one (1) RUS broadband loan indicator that varies over time and counties. Although the value of the loan indicator never takes a value of 1 in those counties without an approved project, the timing of approvals in those counties with approved projects varies over the time period.

Our model can be thought of as a treatment model in which some counties receive a treatment (the RUS broadband loan). Our goal was to estimate whether there is an association between this treatment and measures of economic activity, such as employment, payroll, or the number of establishments. In a treatment evaluation, however, it is important to have an appropriate comparison or control group of untreated subjects, in this case, counties that were not in the service area of a RUS broadband loan. The estimate of the treatment could be in part a reflection of the particular characteristics of those that pursued treatment, in this case those counties that were in the service areas approved for a RUS broadband loan. If those counties were growing faster, or were richer, among other possibilities, then those counties might be expected to continue to grow quickly over the analysis period. If these counties are compared to an average county, it might appear that the broadband loan is associated with the observed pattern of increased economic activity. Alternatively, if the treated counties are compared to other counties that are more similar, the estimated association with the broadband loan might be more modest or nonexistent.

Control Groups

A focus of our estimation approach was to develop a number of different control groups of rural counties without approved broadband loans. We identified three broad types of control groups. First, some control groups are defined using characteristics of the RUS program itself, such as those counties that were in the service areas of projects that were rejected by RUS. These were projects that, we assume, their developers believed would be successful. In this way, the counties in their service areas can be thought of as similar to the set of approved counties in unobservable ways. Second, control groups were defined on the basis of similarity to key observable characteristics of the set of approved counties. We use a proximity-scoring algorithm to match approved counties to other counties based on particular concepts of similarity.

For example, to develop one control group, we looked for counties that were similar to approved counties in terms of economic growth in the period leading up to 2003, the beginning of our analysis period. Third, we defined one control group on the basis of geographic adjacency to the set of counties in approved service areas. This control group may capture less readily observable characteristics of local economic activity in and around the service areas of approved loans.

Rural Definition

Within this estimation framework, a primary issue we considered was which counties to include in our analysis. Although we determined that counties were the best unit of analysis, in some cases they can still be too coarse a level of analysis for any evidence of the RUS loan program's impact to emerge. Accordingly, we used Census data on the rural and urban population characteristics of counties, as well as observations from our site visits (described above in app. I) to identify a suitable universe of counties. One consideration was that the dependent variables of interest in our model (i.e., the economic outcomes) likely scale with county population; that is, the level of employment and payroll, and the number of business establishments will likely increase with a county's population. In some counties that have large rural populations in an absolute sense but also include significant urban centers, the economic activity of the urban areas can overwhelm the activity in the rural portions of the county; these counties may not be well suited for inclusion in a county-level analysis. Our solution to this issue was to restrict the set of analyzed counties to those meeting a rural threshold, so that any changes in economic activity associated with broadband infrastructure had a better chance of being captured with county-level data.

We considered three definitions, and present some program implications of these alternative definitions in table 2. The initial threshold we chose was 90 percent of county population considered rural according to the Census, excluding all counties that are less rural.[86] However, table 2 shows that this threshold had the effect of excluding many counties, including the vast majority of counties with an approved loan. Specifically, there are 289 counties in our data set with an approved loan, but only 52 of them were rural counties defined in this way. Using only a county's rural population has the consequence of treating many counties located in what would typically be thought of as rural areas as not rural because they contain small cities. Based on our site visits we determined that while counties with large Urbanized Area populations were generally too urban to be included in the model, counties with just the smaller Urban Clusters were appropriate. Our preferred threshold for counties was 90 percent of county population considered rural, defined as the sum of rural population and urban cluster population as determined by Census. Table 2 shows that this definition captures almost 90 percent of counties with approved loans.

As an alternative to constructing our own categorization using Census data, we also used the rural–urban continuum codes developed by USDA's Economic Research Service to select rural counties. Specifically, as an alternative, we considered a county to be rural according to these codes if the county was not in a metropolitan area and the urban population of a county was less than 20,000 people. This definition provided a selection of rural counties that fit somewhere between our other two in terms of number of included counties and approximately the same share of counties with approvals as the rural and urban combination definition. We present results for the two Census-based definitions. Results using the USDA definitions were more similar to the rural and urban cluster combination.

Table 2. Number of Counties with Rural Utilities Service (RUS) Loans Using Different Definitions of Rural

Set of Counties	Number of counties	Counties with active RUS loans	Counties with rejected RUS loans	Counties with rescinded RUS loans
All	3,038	289	862	593
90 percent Rural (Census)	671	52	160	41
90 percent Rural plus Urban Cluster (Census)	2,218	253	606	366
Economic Research Service codes	1,576	179	439	231

Source: GAO analysis of RUS loan data and U.S. Census Bureau information.

Note: This analysis reflects counties associated with loans made through the RUS Rural Broadband Access Loan and Loan Guarantee Program. Using RUS data on the proposed service areas of all RUS loan applications through 2011, we categorized each county as part of the service area of an active project, a rejected project, a project for which loan funds had been rescinded by RUS, or not part of any project service area.

Development of Control Groups

Rejected and Rescinded Loans

We developed three types of control groups. First, we developed groups from the program itself, including groups of rejected loan counties and rescinded loan counties. Rejected counties can be thought of as similar to approved counties in terms of intent by broadband providers to build rural broadband infrastructure. Rescinded counties can also be thought of in these terms, but these counties were in service areas that were actually approved for broadband loans.

Matching Counties

Second, we developed control groups based on observable characteristics of counties rather than attributes of the RUS loan program. Specifically, for each approved county we sought to find a non-approved county that is similar. Since there are many dimensions along which counties may be similar to one another, the use of proximity scoring is one way to identify control counties based on how similar they are to approved counties based upon a scoring procedure. In our case, we use logistic regressions on county-level factors that we think could explain whether a county had an approved loan. The proximity score for each county is derived from the logistic regression and reflects the probability that a county has an approved loan based on the set of explanatory variables. We develop two different sets of explanatory variables that we use to calculate proximity scores. The explanatory values are used as independent variables in the proximity scoring logistic regression in which the dependent variable is loan approval. Using the estimated coefficients and the values of the explanatory variables, a proximity score is calculated for each county. We then used a matching algorithm developed by researchers at the Mayo Clinic to select from among the non-approved counties a match for each approved county based on the proximity scores.[87]

We developed different control groups based on two sets of explanatory variables. The first set consisted of annual growth rates in county-level measures of economic activity over the pre-analysis period of 1994— 2002. Specifically, for each county we estimated the annual growth rates in employment, payroll, payroll per employee, and the number of establishments, using County Business Patterns data. We interpreted the matches based on this scoring process to represent a control group that is similar to the set of approved counties based on economic growth profiles in the time period leading up to the start of the broadband loan program in 2003. The second set of explanatory variables consisted of demographic variables from the 2000 Census, again from a time preceding the broadband loan program. Specifically, for each county we examined data on county population, population density, per capita income, the share of county population aged 60 and above, the share of county population that has less than a high school education, and the share of county population that has a college degree or more. We interpreted the matches based on this scoring process to represent a control group that is similar to the set of approved counties based on demographic characteristics that may be related to the costs of providing broadband (population density) as well as characteristics related to the demand for broadband (income, age, and education profiles). Additionally, we developed a control group based on proximity scores using both of these sets of variables in the same scoring regression.

Adjacent Counties

Third, another alternative control group was comprised of the set of rural counties without approved loans that are geographically adjacent to the set of rural counties with approved loans. This set of counties was identified by using the Census county adjacency file for 2010. These adjacent counties are rural, not in the set of approved counties, and adjacent to at least one approved county. These counties included a mix of counties with and without applications.

Results

As discussed above, we used a simple fixed-effects model to estimate the relationship between RUS broadband loans and various annual measures of economic activity at the county level. Since our data consists of 9 annual observations for multiple counties, we have a panel dataset. Our dependent variables are county time series on employment, payroll, and the number of establishments, in log form. We regressed the dependent variables on year and county fixed effects and an indicator variable of whether a county had an approved broadband loan. The loan indicator variable equals 0, except for counties with an approved broadband loan, when, beginning one year after the loan award an all subsequent years, it equals 1.

Our analysis using this model and our preferred definition of rural suggests that RUS broadband loans are associated with a 1 to 4 percent higher level of employment and payroll in affected counties in the year following the loan approval and all subsequent years (see table 3). The estimated effects on payroll were at the higher end of this range. We found no consistent relationship between RUS loans and the number of new business establishments in a community. Our results were much weaker when we restricted the model only to counties that were considered rural using the 90 percent rural population threshold (see table 4), but results were roughly comparable between the samples defined using rural and urban clusters definition and the Economic Research Service continuum codes. Generally speaking, for a given definition of rural counties, our results were consistent across the range of control groups we developed.

As noted above, these model results are broadly consistent with what stakeholders told us, including that broadband access enabled by the RUS loan program can help make businesses more efficient, which can lead to job creation and increased payroll. The lack of effect on the number of establishments, and the modest impact on employment and payroll, may be the result of the county being too coarse a level of analysis for evidence of impact to emerge. Additionally, the effect of the loan program may not be strong enough to affect the number of business establishments at the county level. For instance, while e-commerce is greatly facilitated by broadband access, it could hinder rural businesses by making it cheaper and easier for local residents to shop on-line rather than at local establishments.

Table 3 presents results using the rural and urban cluster definition of rural counties and provides results for the full range of control groups, and table 4 presents results using the rural definition. All of the dependent variables were expressed in log form and the parameter estimate on the loan variable can be interpreted as the percentage increase in the level of economic activity when the loan is in effect.

Though our findings were consistent across various model specifications, our findings require caveats. First, there are no standard metrics for measuring the economic impact broadband access and adoption can have on a community, so our choices in data points may not accurately capture the true value of broadband to rural communities. Second, since RUS broadband loan-project service areas do not conform to county boundaries, our decision to treat all counties containing affected communities as "treated" may mask some very local affects of the broadband loans, or may overstate the extent of some effect. Additionally, regression analysis ascertains relationships, not causality, and models by definition contain a range of uncertainty.

Table 3. Model Results for Counties
90 Percent Rural with Urban Clusters

Control group	Dependent variables (measured in logs)		
	Employment	Payroll	Number of business establishments
Counties with rejected loans			
Parameter estimate	0.016	0.038	0.001
[p-value]	[.052]	[.001]	[.865]
Number of observations	7,731	7,731	7,731
Counties with fully rescinded loans			
Parameter estimate	0.019	0.037	-0.004
[p-value]	[.014]	[.001]	[.365]
Number of observations	5,571	5,571	5,571
Counties matched based on county growth factors			
Parameter estimate	0.017	0.034	0.005
[p-value]	[.032]	[.001]	[.248]
Number of observations	4,536	4,536	4,536
Counties matched based on county demographic factors			
Parameter estimate	0.015	0.032	0.001
[p-value]	[.074]	[.007]	[.891]
Number of observations	4,554	4,554	4,554
Counties matched based on county growth and demographic factors			
Parameter estimate	0.019	0.030	0.007
[p-value]	[.018]	[.007]	[.116]
Number of observations	4,554	4,554	4,554
Counties adjacent to counties with approved loan			
Parameter estimate	0.017	0.029	0.007
[p-value]	[.031]	[.007]	[.080]
Number of observations	6,084	6,084	6,084

Source: GAO analysis based on RUS and Census data.

Notes: This table does not include parameter estimates for the county and year fixed effects. Since the dependent variables are in log form, the parameter estimates represent percentage changes. Additionally, p-values are calculated using robust standard errors that control for heteroskedasticity and within county serial correlation.

Table 4. Model Results for Counties 90 Percent Rural

Control group	Dependent variables (measured in logs)		
	Employment	Payroll	Number of business establishments
Counties with rejected loans			
Parameter estimate	0.019	0.043	-0.004
[p-value]	[.294]	[.054]	[.694]
Number of observations	1,908	1,908	1,908
Counties with fully rescinded loans			
Parameter estimate	-0.013	-0.011	-0.025
[p-value]	[.566]	[.723]	[.057]
Number of observations	837	837	837
Counties matched based on county growth factors			
Parameter estimate	0.012	0.016	-0.004
[p-value]	[.536]	[.486]	[.740]
Number of observations	918	918	918
Counties matched based on county demographic factors			
Parameter estimate	0.037	0.042	-0.003
[p-value]	[.065]	[.163]	[.757]
Number of observations	936	936	936
Counties matched based on county growth and demographic factors			
Parameter estimate	0.010	-0.008	0.006
[p-value]	[.554]	[.720]	[.591]
Number of observations	918	918	918
Counties adjacent to counties with approved loan			
Parameter estimate	0.021	0.014	0.008
[p-value]	[.199]	[.526]	[.435]
Number of observations	954	954	954

Source: GAO analysis based on RUS and Census data.

Notes: This table does not include parameter estimates for the county and year fixed effects. Since the dependent variables are in log form, the parameter estimates represent percentage changes. Additionally, p-values are calculated using robust standard errors that control for heteroskedasticity and within county serial correlation.

End Notes

[1] The term broadband commonly refers to high speed Internet access. GAO, *Telecommunications: Broadband Deployment Is Extensive throughout the United States, but It Is Difficult to Assess the Extent of Deployment Gaps in Rural Areas*, GAO-06-426 (Washington, D.C.: May 5, 2006).

[2] Throughout this report, we refer to entities that have been approved for loans from the RUS loan program as "RUS broadband borrowers." In using this term, we do not refer to borrowers from other RUS loan programs, such as the Telecommunications Infrastructure Loan Program.

[3] The NBM is an online database that allows users to access broadband availability at the neighborhood level. The NBM was created by the National Telecommunications and Information Administration in collaboration with FCC, and in partnership with 50 states, five territories, and the District of Columbia.

[4] Few loans have been approved since 2008, so we determined that sufficient time had passed for most projects financed with RUS loans to have been substantially completed.

[5] Although we obtained, in our view, information from a diverse mix of RUS borrowers, the findings from our site visits cannot be generalized to all borrowers because the sites were selected as part of a nonprobability sample.

[6] *In the Matter of Connect America Fund*, 26 FCC Rcd. 17663, 27 FCC Rcd. 4040 (2011) (report and order and Further Notice of Proposed Rulemaking). In this report we refer to this order as the USF/ICC Transformation Order.

[7] According to FCC, the costs for new fiber broadband construction can range from $11,000 to $24,000 per mile for aerial construction and to $25,000 to $165,000 per mile for buried construction.

[8] See James Prieger, "The Broadband Digital Divide and the Economic Benefits of Mobile Broadband for Rural Areas" (2012). Pepperdine University, *School of Public Policy Working Papers*. Paper 41.

[9] In fiscal year 2001, RUS was directed by statute to administer a pilot broadband program dedicated in part to finance rural broadband infrastructure deployment (*see* Agriculture, Rural Development, Food and Drug Administration, and Related Agencies— Appropriations Act, 2001, Pub. L. No. 106-387, title III, 114 Stat. 1549, 1549A-22 (2000)).

[10] Pub. L. No. 107-171, § 6103, 116 Stat. 134, (2002), codified at 7 U.S.C. § 950bb. In addition to the Rural Broadband Access Loan and Loan Guarantee Program discussed throughout this report, RUS also has a rural telephone loan program (dating back to 1949, now called the Telecommunications Infrastructure Loan Program) that has historically supported infrastructure for telephone voice service. Additionally, the Distance Learning and Telemedicine Grant Program supports broadband-based applications. RUS also administered the Broadband Initiatives Program authorized as part of the American Recovery and Reinvestment Act of 2009, Pub. L. No. 111-5, 123 Stat. 115, 118-119 (Recovery Act).

[11] Rural Broadband Access Loans and Loan Guarantees, 78 Fed. Reg. 8353, 8360 (Feb. 6, 2013); codified at 7 C.F.R. part 1738.

[12] The final rule substantially adopts the interim rule published on March 14, 2011. The 2008 act was the Food, Conservation, and Energy Act of 2008, Pub. L. No. 110-246, § 6102, 122 Stat 1651, 1965 (2008).

[13] 78 Fed. Reg. 8353, 8360 (Feb. 6, 2013). Throughout this report we refer to entities that provide broadband service, including those eligible for RUS loans, as "providers."

[14] These speeds are referred to as the "broadband lending speed," and are a minimum bandwidth requirement for all loans. The 2014 reauthorization act establishes "the minimum acceptable level of broadband service" as at least 4 megabits per second downstream and 1 megabits per second upstream. At least once every 2 years, the Secretary of Agriculture is required to

review and may adjust this speed definition and may consider establishing different minimum speeds for fixed and mobile (wireless) broadband. Agricultural Act of 2014, Pub. L. No. 113-79, § 6104, 128 Stat 649 (2014) to be codified as amending 7 U.S.C. § 950bb(a)(2).

[15] *Id.*

[16] RUS does not have any pending applications.

[17] This requirement was modified by the 2014 reauthorization act to one where not less than 15 percent of the households in the proposed service territory are unserved or have service levels below the minimum acceptable level of broadband service. *Id.* Unserved and underserved areas tend to have conditions that increase the cost of constructing and maintaining broadband networks, and have been defined differently for other federal programs.

[18] Budgeting for the cost of credit programs is governed by the Federal Credit Reform Act of 1990 (Pub. L. No. 101-508, title V, 104 Stat. 1388, 1388-610, codified as amended at 2 U.S.C. § 661-661f), which requires federal agencies to receive and obligate budget authority to cover the estimated long-term cost to the government (which includes defaults, delinquencies, and interest subsidies) of providing credit assistance, calculated on a net present value basis, and excluding administrative costs. Beginning in fiscal year 2005, the loan program has received funds that can be carried over into a subsequent fiscal year. In fiscal years 2005 through 2007, the loan program received funds that were available for 2 fiscal years, and since fiscal year 2008, the funds have been no-year money, and are available until expended or rescinded.

[19] Federal policy has long called for making affordable residential telephone service available to the greatest possible number of Americans—a policy known as "universal service." The Communications Act of 1934 established the nation's telecommunications policy, including making communications services available "so far as possible, to all the people of the United States." The USF programs are primarily funded through mandatory payments from companies providing telecommunications services—payments usually passed along to consumers as a line item fee on their telephone bill.

[20] The High-Cost Program consists of several components, each with different eligibility criteria and different methods to determine the level of support. We refer to all components when referring to the High-Cost Program throughout this report. The other three USF programs subsidize telecommunication services for low-income consumers (Low Income Program), and telecommunication and broadband services for schools and libraries (E-Rate Program) and for rural health care providers (Rural Health Care Program). We have previously reported on FCC's efforts to reform the USF High-Cost Program, which will ultimately be replaced by the Connect America Fund. See GAO, *Telecommunications: FCC Has Reformed the High-Cost Program, but Oversight and Management Could be Improved*, GAO-12-738 (Washington, D.C.: July 25, 2012).

[21] USF/ICC Transformation Order, ¶ 1, 26 FCC Rcd., 17667.

[22] This is the total amount approved by RUS, not necessarily the actual amount paid out by RUS, since some loans are rescinded or reduced or defaulted before all funds were paid out.

[23] This program was intended to finance broadband infrastructure projects, overlapping the agency's other broadband loan programs. For fiscal year 2010, RUS gave priority to the Recovery Act program.

[24] One loan was also awarded to a U.S. territory, the U.S. Virgin Islands. Additionally, not all loans supported projects located in a single state; 20 loans were awarded to communities in multiple states.

[25] We selected our site visits based on a variety of factors, including the size and status of the loan and geographic diversity. See appendix I for more information.

[26] All figures are in 2012 dollars.

[27] U.S. Department of Agriculture, Office of Inspector General, Southwest Region, *Audit Report: Rural Utilities Service Broadband Loan and Loan Guarantee Program,* 09601-8-Te (Washington, D.C.: Mar. 31, 2009).

[28] The 2002 definition required that communities not exceed 20,000 inhabitants and not be within a metropolitan statistical area. Pub. L. No. 107-171, § 601, 116 Stat. 416. In 2004, the definition was loosened to allow some communities within MSAs. Consolidated Appropriations Act of 2004, Pub. L. No. 108-199, § 772, 118 Stat. 3, 40.

[29] Food, Conservation, and Energy Act of 2008, P.L. No. 110-246, § 6110, 122 Stat. 1657, 1960. As we previously stated, eligible areas now include communities of 20,000 or fewer inhabitants that are not within urbanized areas next to a town of greater than 50,000 population. In order to be considered rural by RUS, all communities in the proposed service area of a loan must meet the definition.

[30] U.S. Department of Agriculture, Office of Inspector General, Southwest Region, *Audit Report: Rural Utilities Service Broadband Grant and Loan Programs,* 09601-4-Te (Washington, D.C.: Sept. 30, 2005).

[31] Specifically, 68 percent of active loans meet the 2008 and 79 percent, the 2004 definitions of rural, based on our analysis using 2010 Census data. Only about half, 47 percent, of active loans satisfy the most restrictive criteria—the 2002 definition—used by RUS for the loan program. We did not analyze whether specific loans approved by RUS were not eligible under the relevant definition of rural at the time.

[32] Specifically, 93 percent of active loans fell outside of a 2010 Census urbanized area, and 95 percent, outside of a 2000 Census urbanized area.

[33] RUCA has 10 tiers along the spectrum of rurality, each of which is further broken down into secondary codes. We used the 4-tiered data consolidation recommended for analysis by the Washington State Department of Health. See Washington State Department of Health, *Guidelines for Using Rural-Urban Classification Systems for Public Health Assessment,* revised February 2009.

[34] Specifically, 60 percent of these loans fell into rural categories using the 2013 RUCA codes. We performed this analysis using both 2006 and 2013 RUCA data, and found the loan communities met rurality criteria more often when using the 2013 data, which are based on the 2010 Census.

[35] We did not perform an in depth analysis of the characteristics of a loan more likely to default because this would require us to evaluate details of companies' finances, which was outside the scope of this study. However, of the 18 defaulted loans, the majority was for wireless projects, and many involved companies that have filed for bankruptcy. Overall, loans that defaulted did not involve significantly larger loan amounts than non-defaults.

[36] Specifically, RUS begins by notifying the provider of a missed payment to provide it an opportunity to catch up on payment or develop a repayment plan.

[37] U.S. Department of Agriculture, Office of Inspector General, Southwest Region, *Audit Report: Rural Utilities Service Broadband Grant and Loan Programs,* 09601-4-Te (Washington, D.C.: Sept. 30, 2005). According to RUS officials, RUS disagreed with this finding at the time of the Office of Inspector General report and still disagrees.

[38] The total dollar value of these 18 defaulted loans is $488.2 million, but this represents the total approved loan award. In some cases, RUS did not pay out all of the loan before default. Additionally, RUS may have recovered all of the funding it paid out for these defaulted loans.

[39] Specifically, each approved loan requires, among other things, monitoring of construction, review of quarterly financial reports submitted by providers, and security arrangements.

[40] Currently all program staff work both on awarding and servicing loans.

[41] OMB, *Policies for Federal Credit Programs and Non-Tax Receivables,* OMB Circular No. A-129, § IV.C.(c). (January 2013).

[42] GAO, *Small Business Administration: New Service for Lender Oversight Reflects Some Best Practices, but Strategy for Use Lags Behind,* GAO-04-610 (Washington, D.C.: Jun. 8, 2004).

[43] For a summary of these issues and federal broadband programs, see Congressional Research Service. *Broadband Internet Access and the Digital Divide: Federal Assistance Programs.* (July 17, 2013).

[44] This analysis specifically looked at wireline broadband providers offering advertised download speeds of at least 3 megabits per second. The analysis was conducted at the county level because some individual communities do not have complete data in the NBM. Counties contain multiple communities, each of which may have a unique broadband provider, in addition to larger providers that may be present throughout the county. This can lead to an overall large number of reported providers within the county.

[45] GAO, *Telecommunications: Federal Broadband Deployment Programs and Small Business,* GAO-14-203 (Washington, D.C.: Feb. 7, 2014).

[46] This type of statistical method only suggests correlations between variables and not causation.

[47] Our geographic unit of analysis for this work was the county because counties—more fully than zip codes, though not completely—encompass the geographical extent of local labor markets. For more information on our methodology for this model, see appendix II.

[48] The terms telemedicine and telehealth are often used interchangeably and generally refer to technologies that allow rural patients to receive, through remote access, medical diagnoses or patient care, often from specialists who are located in urban areas or university hospitals. For more information, see GAO, *Telecommunications: FCC's Performance Management Weaknesses Could Jeopardize Proposed Reforms of the Rural Health Care Program,* GAO-11-27 (Washington, D.C.: Nov. 17, 2010).

[49] Pub. L. No. 111-352, 124 Stat. 3866 (2011).

[50] Pub. L. No. 103-62, 107 Stat. 285 (1993).

[51] OMB, *Preparation, Submission, and Execution of the Budget,* Circular No. A-11 (2013).

[52] GAO, *Tax Administration: IRS Needs to Further Refine Its Tax Filing Season Performance Measures,* GAO-03-143 (Washington, D.C.: Nov. 22, 2002). In this report, we developed nine attributes of successful performance goals and measures based on key legislation and other factors. See the report for additional details.

[53] GAO, *Managing For Results: Views on Ensuring the Usefulness of Agency Performance Information to Congress,* GAO/GGD-00-35 (Washington, D.C.: Jan. 26, 2000).

[54] USDA reports that "all applications undergo an extensive review to determine eligibility. Additionally, all approved applications must show feasibility from a financial and technical standpoint. Applicants also are required to perform market surveys of their proposed service areas. Therefore, the data are reliable."

[55] FCC, *Connecting America: The National Broadband Plan* (Mar. 16, 2010), at p. 150.

[56] GAO-03-143.

[57] Throughout this section "USF support" refers to funding from the High-Cost Program. All 30 borrowers noted here received support from the High-Cost Program in at least one year since 2003.

[58] The average amount of USF support for RUS borrowers with active loans, per year (2003-2013), was $1,245,444.

[59] Some USF recipients did not receive any support in some years and later received support.

[60] USF/ICC Transformation Order, ¶¶ 128-133. 26 FCC Rcd., 17712-17715.

[61] *Id.,* ¶¶ 158-168, at pp. 17725-17729.

[62] *Id.,* ¶¶ 25-27, 507, 516-525, at pp. 17674, 17829, 17832-17834.

[63] *Id.,* ¶ 20, at p. 17673.

[64] *Id.,* part XVII, at p. 18045.

[65] *Id.,* ¶ 35, at p. 17676.

[66] These reductions in High Cost Program support could be the result of many factors, including USF reforms as well as decreases in the number of telephone subscribers, since support is tied to the number of lines being served.

[67] FCC recognized in the USF/ICC Transformation Order that ICC reform "was not 100 percent revenue-neutral relative to" prior revenues. *Id.*, ¶ 848, at p. 17956.

[68] *Id.*, ¶ 36, at p.17677.

[69] The Rural Telephone Finance Cooperative also noted in a letter to FCC that "reductions in USF support and/or net operating revenue without adequate transitions and a robust Connect America Fund could make it difficult for telcos to maintain key financial ratios and could lead to a greater likelihood of loan covenant breaches and payment defaults."

[70] Michael J. Balhoff and Bradley P. Williams, *State USF White Paper: New Rural Investment Challenges,* Balhoff & Williams, LLC (June 2013).

[71] Some of this decline in demand is also attributable to the existence of the Recovery Act broadband program, as well as the fact that new regulations for the broadband loan program took effect in March 2011 (Rural Broadband Access Loans and Loan Guarantees, 76 Fed. Reg. 13770 (March 14, 2011) (interim rule)), after which RUS required all pending applications be resubmitted. However, USDA reported in its fiscal year 2012 performance report that "the level of uncertainty caused by the new USF and ICC revisions directly impacted the level of demand for the infrastructure loan program."

[72] *Universal Service Implementation Progress Report*, WC Docket No. 10-90 (Mar. 18, 2014).

[73] 2014 WL 1653217 (April 23, 2014) (News Release), p. 4.

[74] GAO, *Telecommunications: FCC Should Take Steps to Ensure Equal Access to Rulemaking Information*, GAO-07-1046 (Washington, D.C.: Sept. 6, 2007). The rules examined as part of this prior report's case studies took between 1.0 and 4.5 years to complete.

[75] *In re: FCC 11-161*, Docket No. 11-9900 (10th Cir.).

[76] Specifically, Hart et al, "Rural Definitions for Health Policy and Research," *American Journal of Public Health* (95), July 2005; and GAO, *Rural Housing: Changing the Definition of Rural Could Improve Eligibility Determinations*, GAO-05-110 (Washington, D.C.: Dec. 3, 2004).

[77] Portions of the service area for some loan projects were not in communities but in unincorporated areas, about which we only had information about the county that area was in. With no way to map these areas, we excluded them from our review.

[78] The service areas of RUS borrowers must meet RUS's definition of rural, but can take any shape and must not necessarily conform to a political boundary (e.g., Census tract, zip code, county). As a result, "treated" areas (that is, areas part of an approved, fully rescinded, or rejected loan project) do not perfectly overlap areas for which economic outcome data are available (e.g., zip codes, counties). For our purposes throughout this report, we consider an area as "treated" (i.e., having received a loan) or "rejected" (i.e., having a fully rescinded loan or rejected loan application) if any part of it is included in the list of communities affected by the loan.

[79] For our purposes throughout this report, we used county as the geographical region of quantitative analysis because economic development data are not available for some small individual communities. Additionally, counties more fully (although still incompletely) than zip codes or Census tracts encompass the geographical extent of local markets.

[80] National Broadband Map data has been found to misrepresent broadband availability in certain areas, either through providers overstating service areas or overall limited data for certain states. However, we could not identify a reason why these data limitations would systematically impact communities or counties associated with RUS loans so we determined our results would likely not be biased.

[81] *In the Matter of Connect America Fund*, 26 FCC Rcd. 17663, 27 FCC Rcd. 4040 (2011).

[82] Throughout this appendix and report we refer to only loans made through the RUS Rural Broadband Access Loan and Loan Guarantee Program.

[83] GAO, *Empowerment Zone and Enterprise Community Program: Improvements Occurred in Communities, but the Effect of the Program Is Unclear*, GAO-06-727 (Washington, D.C.: Sept. 22, 2006).

[84] Ivan T. Kandilov and Mitch Renkow, *Infrastructure Investment and Rural Economic Development: An Evaluation of USDA's Broadband Loan Program*, Growth and Change: Vol. 41 (2010).

[85] See Jayakar, Krishna and Eun-A Park, *Broadband and Unemployment: Analysis of Cross-sectional Data for U.S. Counties*, paper presented at the Telecommunications Policy Research Conference, 2013. Whitacre, et al., *Broadband's Contribution to Economic Health in Rural Areas: A Causal Analysis and an Assessment of the 'Connected Nation' Program*, paper presented at the Telecommunications Policy Research Conference, 2013.

[86] The Census Bureau's urban-rural classification is a delineation of geographical areas, identifying both individual urban areas and the rural areas of the nation. Census's urban areas represent densely developed territory, and encompass residential, commercial, and other non-residential urban land uses. Urban areas are delineated after each decennial census by applying specified criteria to decennial census and other data. Census identifies two types of urban areas: Urbanized Areas of 50,000 or more people; and Urban Clusters of at least 2,500 and less than 50,000 people.

[87] Specifically, we used the Statistical Analysis System macro 'gmatch', developed by Eric Bergstralh and Jon Kosanke of the Biomedical Statistics and Informatics Division of the Mayo Clinic, available via http://www.mayo.edu/research/departments-divisions/department-health-sciences-research/division-biomedical-statistics-informatics/software/locally-written-sas-macros.

In: Rural Broadband   ISBN: 978-1-63463-215-7
Editor: Clyde L. Horn   © 2014 Nova Science Publishers, Inc.

Chapter 3

RECOVERY ACT: BROADBAND PROGRAMS ARE ONGOING, AND AGENCIES' EFFORTS WOULD BENEFIT FROM IMPROVED DATA QUALITY[*]

United States Government Accountability Office

WHY GAO DID THIS STUDY

Access to affordable broadband service is seen as vital to economic growth and improved quality of life, yet residents in many areas of the country lack accsess to or do not use broadband. To extend broadband access and adoption, the American Recovery and Reinvestment Act of 2009 (Recovery Act) provided over $7 billion to NTIA and RUS for grants or loans to support broadband projects. NTIA and RUS made all awards by September 30, 2010.

This report responds to mandates under the Recovery Act for GAO to examine the use of Recovery Act funds and report on the quarterly estimates of jobs funded. This report addresses (1) the progress of broadband projects, (2) their effect on expanding access to and adoption of broadband, and (3) any challenges awardees face in completing projects and agency actions to address these challenges. GAO analyzed program documentation and data and interviewed agency officials and BTOP and BIP awardees.

---

[*] This is an edited, reformatted and augmented version of the United States Government Accountability Office publication, GAO-12-937, dated September 2012.

WHAT GAO RECOMMENDS

To ensure RUS is collecting reliable information regarding the effect of its investments in broadband, GAO recommends that RUS take steps to improve the quality of its data on the number of fiber miles and wireless access points created by BIP projects. RUS disagreed with GAO's characterization that it does not collect adequate data, and stated it has already taken steps to improve data quality. GAO believes that more reliable data will permit RUS to better assess the progress of the BIP program.

WHAT GAO FOUND

The progress of the broadband projects is difficult to measure because of data limitations. As projects progress, the National Telecommunications and Information Administration (NTIA) and the Rural Utilities Service (RUS) disburse awarded funds to projects on, for example, a reimbursement basis. As of July 2012, NTIA has disbursed approximately $1.9 billion of the $3.8 billion it awarded for projects under the Broadband Technology Opportunities Program (BTOP), and as of June 2012, RUS has disbursed approximately $1 billion of the $3.3 billion it awarded for projects under the Broadband Initiatives Program (BIP). These disbursements are one measure of progress, and the disbursements indicate that the projects in aggregate are less than half complete. However, disbursements sometimes lag behind actual progress for a number of reasons, such as contracts that provide for payment after work is completed. In addition, the agencies have been inconsistent in collecting non-financial data on project progress. While NTIA has collected data on BTOP projects, RUS did not collect data until recently. According to NTIA data, 76 percent of planned network miles are complete. According to RUS, the data it has recently collected are not reliable measures of fiber miles and wireless access points deployed by BIP projects. Without reliable information on the progress of BIP projects in expanding infrastructure, RUS may struggle to demonstrate the progress and effectiveness of the BIP program.

Data limitations make it difficult to fully measure the effect of BTOP and BIP on expanding access to and adoption of broadband. NTIA's non-financial data indicate that BTOP awardees have established over 57,000 new or upgraded network miles, with connections to over 8,000 community anchor institutions, such as schools, libraries, and hospitals, and nearly 34,000 new computer workstations for use in public computer centers, such as libraries. RUS initially did not collect comparable non-financial data for BIP projects, and the data it has are not reliable; therefore, it is not possible to fully assess the effect of BIP on expanding access to broadband. With respect to broadband adoption, however, both NTIA and RUS have faced difficulties collecting reliable data from awardees on subscribership for BTOP and BIP projects. Both agencies have taken steps to address this issue, with NTIA providing guidance to awardees and RUS developing a tool for staff reviews of subscribership data reported by awardees.

Both NTIA and RUS helped awardees address multiple challenges in completing their broadband projects. Specifically, awardees identified challenges complying with regulations and obtaining permits, as well as handling construction-related issues such as broadband fiber shortages. BTOP's non-infrastructure projects— which provide computers to libraries or encourage broadband adoption—faced a different set of challenges, including staffing, contracting, and procurement. NTIA and RUS have taken a number of actions—including providing regular contact and expertise, webinars, and guidance—to help awardees address these challenges. In addition, RUS hired additional staff to address delays in its review and approval of contracts, a challenge that delayed some BIP projects.

ABBREVIATIONS

BIP	Broadband Initiatives Program
BTOP	Broadband Technology Opportunities Program
CCI	Comprehensive Community Infrastructure
FCC	Federal Communications Commission
FPO	Federal Program Officer
GFR	General Field Representative
FTE	full-time equivalent
NTIA	National Telecommunications and Information Administration
OMB	Office of Management and Budget
PCC	public computer center
Recovery Act	American Recovery and Reinvestment Act of 2009
RUS	Rural Utilities Service
SBA	sustainable broadband adoption

September 14, 2012

The Honorable John D. Rockefeller IV
Chairman
The Honorable Kay Bailey Hutchison
Ranking Member
Committee on Commerce, Science, and Transportation
United States Senate

The Honorable Fred Upton
Chairman
The Honorable Henry A. Waxman
Ranking Member
Committee on Energy and Commerce
House of Representatives

Access to affordable broadband telecommunications[1] is increasingly viewed as vital to long-term economic growth and improved quality of life, just as electricity, telephone, and the interstate highway system filled similar roles in previous generations. The ability to share large amounts of information at ever-greater speeds increases productivity, facilitates commerce, and drives innovation. Furthermore, broadband can improve citizens' quality of life. For example, broadband technology makes it possible for a patient to visit a local clinic and receive medical attention from specialists hundreds of miles away, for a student to access information not available from the local library, and for a firefighter to download blueprints of a burning building. Broadband is particularly critical in rural areas, where advanced communications can reduce the isolation of remote communities and individuals.

To extend access to broadband throughout the United States, as well as to stimulate the economy and create jobs, Congress appropriated $7.2 billion for broadband programs under the American Recovery and Reinvestment Act of 2009 (Recovery Act), enacted on February 17, 2009.[2] This $7.2 billion included:

- $4.7 billion for the Department of Commerce's National Telecommunications and Information Administration (NTIA) to create the Broadband Technology Opportunities Program (BTOP) to award competitive grants to a variety of entities for broadband infrastructure, public computer centers, and innovative projects to stimulate demand for and adoption of broadband.[3]

- $2.5 billion for the Department of Agriculture's Rural Utilities Service (RUS) for the Broadband Initiatives Program (BIP) to provide loans, grants, and loan/grant combinations for broadband infrastructure projects primarily in rural areas.[4]

The agencies made all awards by September 30, 2010. As of July 2012, there were 225 BTOP awards comprising $3.8 billion in awarded funds.[5] As of June 2012, there were 263 BIP projects comprising $3.3 billion in awarded funds.[6]

Nearly 2 years have passed since all BTOP and BIP Recovery Act awards were made; thus, this review provides an opportunity to assess the status of the projects. This report is part of GAO's ongoing efforts to monitor Recovery Act programs and builds on our prior reports reviewing BTOP and BIP.[7] In particular, we examined: (1) What progress has been made implementing broadband projects funded by the Recovery Act? (2) What effect, if any, have these projects had on expanding access to and adoption of broadband service? (3) What challenges, if any, do grant and loan recipients face in completing broadband projects and what actions have the agencies taken to help address these challenges? The information provided in this report and in appendix II responds to two recurring mandates in the Recovery Act. The first, which we respond to as part of this report, requires that we review bimonthly, the use of Recovery Act funds by recipients.[8] The second, which we respond to in appendix II, requires us to comment and report quarterly on estimates of jobs funded and counted as full-time equivalents (FTE), as reported by recipients of Recovery Act funds.[9]

To address our objectives, we reviewed program data collected by NTIA and RUS, interviewed agency officials and program awardees, and reviewed relevant documentation. Specifically, to determine the progress made implementing broadband projects, we analyzed the data collected by NTIA and RUS on the total funding awarded and the amount of funds disbursed to each project. We also reviewed NTIA's data on the progress made in meeting BTOP's program targets related to deploying infrastructure; RUS did not collect comparable data until recently, and could not assure the quality of its data. To assess the effect of the projects on expanding access to and adoption of broadband service, we analyzed the data reported by BTOP awardees on the number of network miles deployed (which can include miles of broadband fiber and non-fiber miles, such as microwave links), institutions connected, computer workstations installed in public computer centers, and broadband subscribers. We also interviewed BTOP and BIP awardees to understand the effects of their individual projects; we selected awardees to interview that varied in progress (gauged by the percentage of their total award that had been disbursed), and that were geographically dispersed. We also selected awardees who received large awards. To determine the challenges that grant and loan recipients face in completing projects, we interviewed NTIA and RUS officials, as well as BTOP and BIP awardees. We also reviewed BTOP awardees' progress reports for the first quarter of 2012, in which awardees noted challenges or issues they were facing in achieving planned progress. For BIP, we reviewed a tracking spreadsheet maintained by RUS where agency officials note the status of each BIP project and, in some cases, would note issues or challenges facing individual projects. To determine the reliability of the data used in this report, we reviewed relevant documentation, including manuals, guidance, and forms provided to awardees reporting the data, descriptions of internal controls, and Inspector General reviews of the data from the Department of Agriculture and the Department of the Treasury (which manages the payment system used by BTOP recipients). We also interviewed agency officials about their processes for reviewing the data and ensuring their accuracy. We found the data generally reliable for our purposes and note the limitations of the data where appropriate. For more information on our scope and methodology, see appendix I.

We conducted this performance audit from November 2011 through September 2012 in accordance with generally accepted government auditing standards. Those standards require that we plan and perform the audit to obtain sufficient, appropriate evidence to provide a reasonable basis for our findings and conclusions based on our audit objectives. We believe that the evidence obtained provides a reasonable basis for our findings and conclusions based on our audit objectives.

BACKGROUND

In addition to being administered by different agencies, BTOP and BIP differ in several ways, including in methods for providing funding to awardees, types of awardees funded, and services funded through the programs. NTIA funded a range of organizations from states and municipalities to non-profit and commercial organizations, whereas RUS made BIP loans, grants, and combinations of loans and grants primarily to private-sector entities, including for-profit companies and cooperatives. In addition to funding infrastructure projects, BTOP funded public computer center (PCC) projects and sustainable broadband adoption (SBA) projects. Also, the vast majority of BTOP's infrastructure awards were investments in "middle-mile" infrastructure projects, which provide a link from the Internet backbone to the last mile networks of local providers (such as cable or phone companies) that provide broadband service to end users. The availability of broadband service to end users depends upon access to adequate middle-mile facilities, which can be costly to deploy in rural areas. In contrast, BIP primarily funded "last-mile" infrastructure projects that provide service directly to end users. Table 1 provides more detail about the BTOP and BIP programs, including the current number of projects and the amount of funding they represent.

NTIA and RUS solicited applications to the programs and made awards in two rounds, with the first funding round beginning in June 2009 and ending in April 2010, and the second round beginning in January 2010 and ending in September 2010. In the joint *Notice of Funds Availability*, NTIA and RUS provided that projects should be substantially complete within 2 years of receiving an award. The agencies disburse awarded funds as projects progress. To meet the substantially complete requirement, a project must receive two-thirds of its award 2 years after receiving the award.[10] NTIA and RUS also provided that projects should be complete within 3 years of receiving an award. In October 2011, RUS modified these requirements to provide that BIP projects must commence within 180 days of the latter of the completion of the project's historic preservation or environmental review, and be fully complete no later than June 30, 2015. NTIA maintained the original requirements. Since NTIA made several rounds of awards, the 3-year completion deadlines for the projects are staggered throughout 2012 and 2013. Table 2 shows the various deadlines, and the number of BTOP projects subject to that deadline.

NTIA and RUS must oversee BTOP and BIP projects, respectively, through each program's completion. NTIA and RUS both have officials monitoring the overall progress of the programs and reviewing requests for funds. In addition to these officials, the agencies also provided staff to serve as the primary point-of-contact for their awardees and answer questions and address issues that arise for specific awardees. NTIA's Federal Program Officers (FPO) provide this assistance to BTOP awardees; RUS's General Field Representatives (GFR) serve the same role for BIP awardees. In addition, BTOP and BIP awardees face a variety of reporting requirements. For example, the Recovery Act requires fund recipients, including BTOP and

BIP awardees, to submit quarterly reports that provide a description of their projects or activities, the progress of their projects, and estimates of the number of resulting jobs funded, measured on a FTE basis.[11] NTIA also requires that BTOP awardees submit quarterly and annual progress reports to the agency that provide financial data and information on the projects' status and effects. RUS requires that BIP awardees submit quarterly reports that provide subscribership data, and according to RUS, these efforts also include financial statements consisting of income statements, balance sheets, and cash flow statements.

Table 1. Summary of Recovery Act Broadband Programs, as of June and July 2012

Program	Project category[a]	Number of projects	Total program funds	Description
BTOP	*Comprehensive community infrastructure*	117	$3.4 billion	Deploy broadband infrastructure. NTIA primarily funded middle-mile projects, which do not provide service to end users (such as households and businesses), but instead provide a link from the Internet backbone to the networks of local service providers, such as cable or phone companies. The projects also provide new or upgraded connections to community anchor institutions, such as schools, libraries, colleges and universities, medical and healthcare providers, public safety entities, and other community support organizations. Seven of these awards fund projects that intend to use the 700 MHz spectrum to deploy public safety broadband systems.[b]
	Public computer center	65	$200 million	Expand public access to broadband service and enhance broadband capacity at entities such as community

Program	Project category[a]	Number of projects	Total program funds	Description
				colleges and public libraries. Awardees also provide classes at these entities, in which citizens can receive training on topics such as online job searching, basic computer and Internet skills, and certification and educational courses.
	Sustainable broadband adoption	43	$250 million	Increase Internet use and broadband subscribership among individuals and businesses. Projects may include digital literacy training and outreach campaigns to increase the relevance of broadband in people's everyday lives.
BIP	*Infrastructure and satellite*	263	$3.3 billion	Deploy infrastructure in rural areas, with an emphasis on last-mile infrastructure. A last-mile project is defined as any project that provides service to end users or end-users' devices. Four of these awards fund satellite broadband projects, which offer satellite broadband connections to users in rural locations where terrestrial broadband services are not available. Twelve awards funded middle-mile projects.

Source: GAO analysis of NTIA (as of July 2012) and RUS (as of June 2012) data.

Note: Canceled projects removed from totals.

[a] We excluded certain activities funded under BTOP and BIP, such broadband mapping projects and funds transferred to FCC for the national broadband plan under BTOP and technical assistance projects funded under BIP.

[b] In February 2012, Congress enacted the Middle Class Tax Relief and Job Creation Act of 2012, Pub. L. No. 112-96, § 6002, 126 Stat 156, 203 (2012), codified at 47 U.S.C. § 1422, which contained provisions to create a nationwide interoperable public safety broadband network, with one entity holding the license for the 700 MHz spectrum. In light of this development, NTIA partially suspended the seven

BTOP-funded 700 MHz public safety projects to ensure that they proceed in a manner that supports development of the nationwide, interoperable network.

Table 2. Deadlines for BTOP Projects

Deadline	Total award value (in millions)	Number of BTOP projects subject to deadline			
		Comprehensive community infrastructure	Public computer center	Sustainable broadband adoption	Total
November 2012	$64	2	4	2	**8**
December 2012	$71	2	2	1	**5**
January 2013	$533	24	11	3	**38**
February 2013	$212	7	3	6	**16**
March 2013	$110	5	0	1	**6**
June 2013	$440	18	11	0	**29**
July 2013	$1,463	43	15	9	**67**
August 2013	$864	16	12	14	**42**
September 2013	$46	0	7	7	**14**
Total	**$3,803**	**117**	**65**	**43**	**225**

Source: GAO analysis of NTIA data.

Note: Canceled projects removed from totals. April and May 2013 are not included because none of the BTOP projects have a deadline occurring in those months.

THE PROGRESS OF RECOVERY ACT BROADBAND PROJECTS IS DIFFICULT TO MEASURE BECAUSE OF DATA LIMITATIONS

NTIA and RUS both use the amount of funds disbursed to awardees as one method of tracking progress, and less than half of all the awarded funding has been disbursed to Recovery Act BTOP and BIP awardees. BTOP awardees appear to have made more progress than BIP awardees, as NTIA has disbursed half of BTOP's funds while RUS has disbursed less than one-third of BIP's funds. However, the agencies disburse awarded funds for projects as payment becomes due, sometimes only as contracts are complete. Because disbursements do not fully reflect the amount of work completed, NTIA has established other non-financial indicators of progress, such as network miles deployed. In contrast, RUS did not initially establish indicators to measure the deployment of infrastructure.

Amount of Funding Disbursed as an Indicator of Progress

As awardees implement their projects, they request funds from the agency administering their award. NTIA and RUS track how much of each project's award that they have disbursed to the awardee, which serves as one indicator of progress. The data that NTIA and RUS collect indicate that the agencies have disbursed less than half of all awarded funds. Of the roughly $3.8 billion available for the BTOP projects, NTIA has disbursed approximately $1.9 billion (50 percent) to its awardees. As noted in figure 1, disbursements to NTIA's infrastructure projects comprise $1.6 billion of BTOP's disbursed funds, while disbursements to public computer center and sustainable broadband adoption projects total $290 million. Of the roughly $3.3 billion available for the BIP projects, RUS has disbursed approximately $1 billion (30 percent) to its awardees.

Our analysis of the disbursements indicates that BTOP awardees have made more progress than BIP awardees. Sixty-eight percent of BTOP awardees have received more than half of their awarded funds, versus 24 percent of BIP awardees. The fact that the BTOP program includes non-infrastructure projects, such as public computer center and sustainable broadband adoption projects, may partially explain this disparity; NTIA officials noted that since most of these non-infrastructure projects are not required to undergo an environmental assessment, they tend to progress more quickly than the infrastructure projects. See table 3.

Of the BTOP projects that have reached the 2-year target to be substantially complete, more than half have received two-thirds of their total award. As previously mentioned, NTIA provided that BTOP projects should receive two-thirds of their total award within 2 years of receiving the award. There are 102 projects that started before August 2010 and thus have reached the two-thirds benchmark in terms of project time elapsed. Of these 102 projects, 61 have received two-thirds of their awarded funds as of July 2012. NTIA officials told us that in cases where a project does not meet the two-thirds complete threshold, NTIA program officers follow up to determine whether the project is delayed, or whether disbursements are not reflecting the amount of work completed, as mentioned above. In these cases, program officers will conduct a hands-on review, which helps NTIA determine whether the project needs a performance improvement plan with specific actionable recommendations to get the project back on track.

While disbursements are one measure of progress, officials from NTIA and RUS told us that disbursements do not fully reflect the amount of work completed. NTIA and RUS disburse awarded funds for projects as payment becomes due, sometimes only as contracts are completed. Thus disbursements do not fully reflect the amount of work completed at any point in time. NTIA officials noted that in some cases, awardees have entered into contracts that are structured so that the awardee does not pay the contractor until the bulk of construction is complete. For example, one awardee we interviewed noted that although the project was 95 percent complete, it had only received 65 percent of the project's funding, giving the incorrect impression that the project was behind schedule. In our review of BTOP awardees' first quarter 2012 reports to NTIA, we found that some recipients cited this issue when reporting their financial progress in the quarterly reports. Others noted that cost savings made their disbursements appear as if the project were behind schedule, but that was not the case. In other words, a project that is on schedule but incurring costs below the levels anticipated in its original plan could appear to be behind schedule, since its disbursements will be lower than expected.

Table 3. Distribution of BTOP and BIP Awardees by the Percentage of Project Funding Disbursed, as of June and July 2012

Percent of project funding disbursed	BTOP		BIP	
	No. of awardees	Percentage of awardees	No. of awardees	Percentage of awardees
0%	2	1%	15	6%
Greater than 0% to 25%	15	7%	132	50%
Greater than 25% to 50%	55	24%	52	20%
Greater than 50% to 75%	89	40%	27	10%
Greater than 75% to less than 100%	59	26%	30	11%
100%	5	2%	7	3%
Total	**225**	**100%**	**263**	**100%**

Source: GAO analysis of NTIA (as of July 2012) and RUS (as of June 2012) data.
Note: Canceled projects removed from totals.

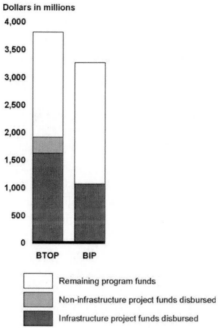

Source: GAO Analysis of NTIA (as of July 2012) and RUS (as of June 2012) data.
Note: Canceled projects removed from totals.

Figure 1. Amount of Awarded Program Funds Disbursed to Current BTOP and BIP
Awardees, and Remaining Program Funds, as of June and July 2012.

Non-Financial Indicators of Progress

NTIA established other non-financial performance measures that show
that awardees have made progress in implementing their projects. Specifically,
NTIA established performance metrics for measuring BTOP's progress against
key performance indicators, such as the number of network miles deployed
and leased, community anchor institutions connected, new workstations in
public computer centers, and new broadband subscribers. NTIA established
the baselines for these key performance indicators by aggregating the
information awardees provided in their applications to the program, and
provided program targets to the Office of Management and Budget (OMB).[12]
NTIA tracks progress against these indicators and reports that as many as 76
percent of network miles are complete and more than 97 percent of new
workstations are complete. These results, when compared with the amount of

funds disbursed, are consistent with NTIA's statements that in some cases, disbursement of funds lags behind progress of projects.

In contrast, RUS did not establish non-financial performance metrics for measuring BIP's progress in deploying infrastructure, such as miles deployed.[13] RUS officials told us that because of RUS's traditional role as a loan administrator, it tends to focus on ensuring that the funding is disbursed, the project is built, and the agency is repaid, instead of tracking project outcome information. In addition, the Recovery Act did not require RUS to collect performance metrics from awardees. Nevertheless, the Recovery Act sought to provide an unprecedented level of transparency with respect to how funds were being spent and program outcomes were being achieved, and we have noted the importance of collecting complete, accurate, and consistent data to document program performance. In June 2012, RUS officials told us that they began tracking the number of fiber miles and wireless access points deployed by BIP projects; however, they could not ensure the quality of the data at that time. Without reliable information on the progress of BIP projects in expanding infrastructure and moving toward completion of projects, RUS may not be able to demonstrate the progress and effectiveness of the BIP program.

NTIA HAS EXPANDED ACCESS TO BROADBAND THROUGH BTOP PROJECTS; HOWEVER, DATA LIMITATIONS MAKE IT DIFFICULT TO MEASURE THE EFFECTS OF BTOP AND BIP ON BROADBAND ADOPTION

NTIA collects data on network miles deployed, community anchor institutions connected, and workstations added at public computer centers, which helps illustrate that BTOP expanded broadband infrastructure and provided increased access to the public. As previously mentioned, RUS did not begin collecting this type of information until this year and cannot assure the quality of the data; thus, BIP's contribution to these goals is less clear. Both NTIA and RUS face challenges in ensuring the quality of subscribership data, and therefore, it is difficult to measure the effect of BTOP and BIP on broadband adoption.

BTOP Expanded Infrastructure and Provided Access at Public Computer Centers

As previously mentioned, the current goal of BTOP's Comprehensive Community Infrastructure (CCI) projects is to deploy or upgrade 75,000 miles of broadband infrastructure and provide broadband access to 15,000 community anchor institutions, such as schools, libraries, health care providers, and public safety entities. As of March 31, 2012, BTOP's 117 infrastructure projects reported that they have established over 57,000 new or upgraded network miles, with connections to over 8,000 community anchor institutions. See table 4.

As shown in table 4, BTOP projects report several different types of miles of broadband infrastructure:

- "Network miles installed" includes newly constructed miles, such as new aerial or buried fiber, built using BTOP funds.
- "Network miles leased" includes new network capacity acquired via lease using BTOP funds.
- "Existing network miles upgraded" refers to existing capacity that was upgraded using BTOP funds.
- "Existing network miles leased" refers to capacity that was acquired from a third-party prior to BTOP and that is being used or improved using BTOP funds.

Table 4. BTOP Infrastructure Expansion, as of March 31, 2012

Miles	
Network Miles Installed	14,192
Network Miles Leased	27,207
Existing Miles Upgraded	13,327
Existing Miles Leased	2,523
Total	**57,249**
Community Anchor Institutions	
Institutions with New Access	2,420
Institutions with Improved Access	5,952
Total	**8,372**

Source: GAO analysis of NTIA data.

Source: GAO.

Figure 2. Example of an Accessible Workstation, with Desktop Magnifier.

In our discussions with BTOP awardees, they explained how their individual projects expanded broadband access in their communities. For example, one awardee who received BTOP and BIP funds explained that the majority of the areas served by its projects did not have broadband service, with one community lacking basic telephone service. The awardee added that as broadband expands in the area, the local economy has benefited as tourism-oriented businesses are better able to provide Web sites and online reservation systems. Another awardee noted that its project serves some areas that previously had broadband service; however, the choice of service provider was limited, and the broadband options were generally expensive and slow. This awardee reported that its BTOP-funded infrastructure improved broadband speed for community anchor institutions, including schools, community colleges, and health care providers, from 1 gigabyte per second to 10 gigabytes per second.

Interviewees also reported that the public computer center (PCC) program expanded access to broadband in their communities. BTOP's 65 PCC projects have deployed new workstations (computers) at multiple locations, such as community colleges and public libraries, throughout a city or state. For example, the New Jersey State Library reported that its PCC project has deployed 845 computers to 124 public libraries, and 128 laptops that community colleges use to provide workforce development courses to the public. Some public computer centers also received upgraded broadband connections and wireless routers. Officials from the State Library of Louisiana noted that residents will use wireless hot spots in the library to access the Internet from their own devices, adding that one woman brings her children to the library parking lot after hours so that they can access the signal and work on their homework when the library is closed. In addition, PCC projects have installed workstations designed to be accessible by users with visual impairments. The workstation in figure 2 includes software that reads aloud what is on the computer screen, screen magnification software, and a desktop magnifier that enlarges materials placed under it. As of March 2012, PCC awardees reported that they provided nearly 34,000 new workstations for public use.

Example of PCC Project: State Library of Louisiana

This PCC project provides classes at local libraries throughout the state. Louisiana residents register in advance for the classes, which typically last an entire day.
Topics include computer basics, software training on Microsoft and Adobe programs, job search, résumé, and interview skills, and business skills, such as accounting and customer service. The project is also using BTOP funds to support a number of electronic resources, such as Homework Louisiana – a free online tutoring service for Louisiana students attending kindergarten through college. Students can receive individual tutoring in math, science, social studies, and English. In addition, Louisiana's Jobs and Career Center portal provides job search and small business resources, and the Learning Express Library provides study guides and practice tests for GED, college, graduate school, as well as professional licensure and certifications.

Total award funding: $8,797,668

PCC projects have also provided classes on a variety of topics, including English as a second language, digital literacy, and job training. Officials from the New Jersey State Library project noted that while they initially targeted people with limited or no computer skills and provided basic computer training, they encountered unexpectedly high demand and expanded course offerings to reach recent college graduates, those with managerial experience, as well as offering additional resources for small businesses and entrepreneurs. We visited classes in Louisiana and Washington, D.C., and observed participants learning software programs. The State Library of Louisiana noted in its first quarter 2012 report that its various training programs had over 19,000 participants. During our visit, we observed a training class, and participants stated that they had driven several hours to attend some classes, and wanted to attend more. For more information see, the sidebar titled "Example of PCC Project: State Library of Louisiana."

Measurement and Data Limitations Make It Difficult to Assess the Programs' Effects on Broadband Adoption

NTIA and RUS have faced difficulties in ensuring that awardees provide reliable data regarding broadband subscribership for their BTOP and BIP projects, which makes it challenging to fully and accurately determine the effects of the programs on broadband adoption. NTIA's sustainable broadband adoption (SBA) projects were established to stimulate demand for broadband Internet access, and applicants were required to describe how they would calculate subscribership for their projects. For example, the SBA project Computers for Youth/Los Angeles Unified School District Broadband Engagement Program provides 4-hour workshops in high-poverty Los Angeles schools, during which it provides hands-on, bilingual training to sixth-grade students and their families on using broadband for educational purposes. The participants receive a free computer pre-loaded with educational software as well as access to toll-free bilingual help-desk support, and Computers for Youth conducts a survey before and after the workshop to determine whether the families subscribed to broadband service after attending the workshop. Computers for Youth stated in its first quarter 2012 report that over 30,000 participants (students and their parents) had attended a family-learning workshop during the course of its program and that nearly 5,000 households had newly subscribed to broadband. Program officials noted that by highlighting the relevance of broadband to children's education and offering free computers and technical support, they were able to generate broadband subscribers despite the lack of discounted broadband service.

Although current data reflect an increase in subscribers as a result of BTOP projects, they may not be accurate. As of March 31, 2012, SBA projects reported that they generated over 334,000 broadband subscribers. However, NTIA officials told us that many recipients have faced difficulties in measuring broadband subscribers related to the project and have revised their counting methods. Thus, NTIA officials noted that the total subscribers reported to date may not represent the true number of new subscribers. In our review of awardees' first quarter 2012 reports, we found that 13 of 43 SBA projects reported difficulties with collecting subscriber data. For example, some awardees reported that they thought they would be able to obtain subscribership data from Internet service providers to determine the effect of their projects, but later found that Internet service providers were unwilling to provide subscribership data. NTIA has provided training on this issue, and facilitated sessions in which projects share best practices for measuring subscribership. Program officials told us NTIA is also working with individual projects to help them find ways to address the challenges involved in collecting subscribership data.

Similarly, RUS data on the effects of BIP projects on broadband adoption may not be accurate. RUS established a goal for BIP projects to provide new or improved broadband service to 359,450 subscribers, and in 2010, RUS stated that it exceeded this goal because it estimates that BIP projects will provide new or improved service to 847,239 subscribers. However, this total does not reflect actual program outcomes, because it is based on the estimates of applicants prior to the execution of their funded projects. RUS requires recipients to report quarterly on the number of households, businesses, educational providers, libraries, health care providers, and public safety providers receiving new or improved broadband service. However, when we reviewed the data, we noted discrepancies. When we asked RUS about these discrepancies in the subscribership data, RUS officials noted that the data are inaccurate and that RUS has implemented quality checks to improve the information. Specifically, RUS developed a spreadsheet tool that RUS staff use to review the subscriber data submitted by individual projects, note whether the data appear to be correct, and report how any problems with the data were resolved. In its comments on a draft version of this report, RUS noted that its field staff provides extensive contact and guidance to awardees.

NTIA AND RUS HAVE ACTED TO ADDRESS THE VARIETY OF CHALLENGES AWARDEES IDENTIFIED IN COMPLETING PROJECTS

BTOP and BIP awardees identified multiple challenges in completing projects, including compliance with regulations and construction related challenges. Additionally, BIP awardees identified some additional challenges related to RUS's processes and requirements, and non-infrastructure projects participating in BTOP face challenges related to staffing and deploying the projects. In some cases, these challenges have contributed to the lack of progress discussed above. NTIA and RUS have taken a number of actions to help awardees address these challenges, including providing awardees with regular contact, expertise, webinars, and guidance.

Challenges

While BTOP and BIP awardees have identified some of the same challenges they have faced, they also identified some different challenges because the programs are administered by different agencies and fund different services. Table 5 lists the challenges we identified facing BTOP and BIP awardees based on our interviews and content analysis of NTIA and RUS documents.

NTIA and RUS officials and awardees all identified challenges associated with environmental compliance, as BTOP and BIP awardees were required to comply with the National Environmental Policy Act[14] and the National Historic Preservation Act.[15] This involved working with state and federal agencies to address any environmental or historic preservation issues related to the project before construction could commence. According to our analysis of BTOP awardees' first quarter 2012 reports to NTIA, 44 of 114 infrastructure awardees reported challenges associated with the environmental assessment and historic preservation review.[16] Likewise, RUS officials told us that the environmental assessment process took significantly longer than anticipated and stated that one cause of this was a backlog within the state offices that conduct the assessments because of the large volume of Recovery Act work. The initial environmental assessment process was also the most common challenge cited by RUS's GFRs, who told us that these assessments took longer than anticipated and negatively affected all awardees' schedules. Officials from NTIA and RUS both noted delays associated with the environmental assessment process, and NTIA officials noted that these delays have been up to 6 months for BTOP projects.

BTOP and BIP awardees reported facing other delays in beginning project construction, such as:

- *Prevailing wage requirements.* The Recovery Act requires that all laborers and mechanics employed by contractors and subcontractors on projects funded directly by or assisted in whole or in part by and through the federal government under the Recovery Act be paid at prevailing wage rates.[17] NTIA and RUS officials and an awardee told us that in many cases identifying the prevailing wage for activities such as fiber deployment was difficult because that type of work had often not been done in that area and the prevailing wage had not yet been determined by the Department of Labor.

Table 5. Challenges Faced by BTOP and BIP Awardees

Challenges	BTOP	BIP
Environmental review and compliance	X	X
Prevailing wage requirements	X	X
Permitting, right of way, and make-ready work	X	X
Weather and terrain	X	X
Broadband fiber availability	X	X
Approval of contracts and plans by RUS		X
Compliance with RUS reporting requirements		X
Proposed changes to the Federal Communications Commission's Universal Service Fund		X
Staffing or expertise	X[a]	
Contracting, procurement, and financing	X[a]	
Technical issues	X[a]	
Outreach and program participation	X[a]	

Source: GAO analysis of interviews and NTIA and RUS documents.

[a] These challenges were identified as pertaining to BTOP PCC and SBA projects.

- *Permitting, right-of-way agreements, and make-ready work.* Awardees must apply for and receive permits and right of way agreements before beginning construction. NTIA officials and awardees told us that for some projects, obtaining these agreements from all the relevant stakeholders took longer than anticipated and put the projects behind schedule. For example, these agreements may have to be obtained from state and local governments, tribal governments, federal entities (such as the Bureau of Land Management), private landowners, and railroads. One awardee we spoke with experienced delays of up to 9 months in the installation of equipment and fiber because of the amount of time it took to receive right of way permits from railroad companies. In addition, make-ready work, which includes the tasks associated with preparing utility poles for the installation of equipment and fiber, must be complete before any construction occurs, and this need has posed challenges to maintaining project timelines. For example, one BTOP awardee indicated in its first quarter 2012 report to NTIA that "keeping make-ready completion ahead of construction crew availability remains the major challenge for the project."

- *Weather, terrain, and broadband fiber availability.* Weather-related challenges and difficult terrain can cause delays in construction. Awardees reported delays for, among other things, a major tornado that caused damage to a service area and equipment, hurricanes, snowfall, and flooding. Difficult terrain can also cause delays. One awardee told us that its project unexpectedly called for boring through solid granite under a river, which required additional tools and time. NTIA and RUS officials told us that BTOP and BIP projects were also delayed due to fiber shortages caused by the 2011 tsunami in Japan and increased worldwide demand for fiber. For example, one BTOP infrastructure awardee noted in its first quarter 2012 report to NTIA that it was "experiencing delays in the delivery of the fiber…[and that] while we received a few shipments during this quarter it was much less than promised."

RUS officials also noted some challenges specific to the BIP program, such as:

- *Approval of contracts and plans.* RUS officials told us that to ensure quality construction is completed, they require that awardees gain approval of contracts before the construction begins or materials are purchased. RUS officials said that on average, it takes the agency 1 and a half months to 2 months to approve a contract. However, some RUS GFRs and awardees said that RUS did not approve BIP contracts in a timely fashion in some instances, which resulted in project delays. In particular, some GFRs said that RUS took 6 to 12 months to approve a contract. RUS officials noted that there could be a number of reasons why contracts had not been approved, including that the contracts were not correct when they were submitted for approval.

- *Compliance with reporting requirements.* RUS officials told us some awardees that received a loan or loan/grant combination have experienced challenges complying with RUS reporting requirements. The officials explained that awardees who had not previously borrowed from RUS are more likely to experience difficulties complying with reporting requirements than those awardees with a history of borrowing from RUS.

- *Proposed changes to the Federal Communications Commission's (FCC) Universal Service Fund.* Some RUS officials were concerned about how reforms to FCC's Universal Service Fund, which provides telecommunications funding to some BIP awardees, could potentially affect projects' income streams. FCC's reforms include changes to the distribution and use of Universal Service Fund payments to make the funds available to support both telephone service and broadband deployment.[18] As a result of the reforms, rural telecommunications carriers could receive reduced universal service support payments. In August 2011, RUS provided data to FCC on how these changes could potentially affect the income stream of RUS borrowers and grant awardees. Subsequently, in its 2011 *Order and Further Notice of Proposed Rulemaking* on this issue, FCC stated that the reforms it adopted were more modest than the estimates used by RUS to determine the potential impact of the reforms, and that RUS did not consider the potential for borrowers to adopt operational efficiencies that would offset reductions in universal service support.[19]

NTIA officials and awardees also identified challenges that apply to non-infrastructure BTOP projects, such as:

- *Staffing or expertise.* PCC and SBA projects faced staffing and expertise challenges, such as high staff turnover, or the need for additional staff to handle tasks such as providing technical support for computers or manning computer labs. Our analysis of BTOP awardees' first quarter 2012 reports to NTIA indicate that 7 of 43 SBA projects and 22 of 64 PCC projects reported challenges with either a lack of staff or lack of staff expertise.

- *Contracting, procurement, and financing.* Contracting and procurement issues also commonly caused delays at the beginning of PCC and SBA projects, according to NTIA officials. These projects can be run by state or local entities, and four of the Federal Program Officers (FPOs) we spoke with told us that the projects they oversee were delayed by the need to comply with state or local contracting or procurement requirements. For example, FPOs told us that one project was delayed by 4 to 5 months because the state legislature needed to approve the spending of BTOP funding, and another project run by a large city was delayed by more than a year because of its internal contracting process.

- *Technical issues.* Issues related to equipment, software, and Internet service, have also been challenging to SBA and PCC projects. Our analysis of BTOP awardees' first quarter 2012 reports to NTIA indicate that 8 of 43 SBA projects and 16 of 64 PCC projects noted challenges with the technical aspects of the projects. For example, one awardee reported that software conflicts caused system crashes for the workstations deployed for seniors and adults with disabilities.

- *Outreach and program participation.* Some awardees reported outreach and participation challenges, such as difficulty in participant retention. For example, one awardee reported that most of the participants were senior citizens and were easily discouraged when they felt that they could not retain new skills after each class or training session. Overall, according to our analysis of BTOP awardees' first quarter 2012 reports to NTIA, 13 of 43 SBA projects and 10 of 64 PCC projects reported challenges related to outreach or participation.

Agencies' Actions to Address Challenges

NTIA and RUS provided resources and took action to help awardees address their challenges. Both agencies have provided awardees with regular contact and support. For example, NTIA officials told us that they have regularly scheduled calls between awardees and FPOs to encourage dialog and early resolution of problems. The officials also noted they have encouraged awardees to come to the agency for help, especially in complex situations where federal influence can help resolve challenges. For example, NTIA officials stated that they worked with FCC and state public utility commissions to ensure that they prioritized their review of BTOP projects' requests for permits. Likewise, RUS officials told us that GFRs and other agency staff have provided regularly scheduled contact to determine project status and challenges early on so they can begin addressing them. Both FPOs and GFRs told us that they worked to identify options for dealing with fiber shortages and provided that information to awardees.

Both NTIA and RUS developed webinars and training sessions to inform awardees and provide them with updated information. NTIA has provided guidance to awardees through webinars and conference calls and has held several webinars on topics including pole attachment issues, computer recycling and refurbishing, and numerous other topics. Some awardees told us the webinars and conference calls were both useful and timely. RUS also developed and held webinars focused on assisting grant and loan recipients with the contract process; which according to officials, could increase the likelihood that the contracts are approved more expeditiously so that awardees can be reimbursed in a more timely fashion. NTIA also has a monitoring process to identify projects with schedule, performance, or other challenges, and as needed provides such projects with performance improvement plans and corrective action plans. In its comments on a draft version of this report, RUS noted that it has implemented a detailed review process to identify issues with BIP awards and is constantly providing guidance and assistance to the awardees to overcome issues with the performance of the award.

In addition to providing the general resources and actions described above, NTIA and RUS took the following actions to address some of the specific challenges described earlier in this report:

- NTIA took steps to facilitate the sharing of information and best practices among projects by identifying projects that had already successfully addressed a particular issue and asking them to share their experiences with similar projects. For example, a significant number of infrastructure projects were experiencing similar make-ready challenges, and NTIA organized and moderated a discussion where awardees discussed problems and solutions.

- NTIA also created different groups for PCC and SBA projects to share information on a range of issues that were challenging awardees related to K-12 education, seniors, tribes, municipalities, and healthcare.
- RUS proposed contract modifications to streamline and simplify the timeline for construction and hired 8 additional engineers and loan and grant technicians and allowed some GFRs overseeing larger projects to approve routine contracts to help address the contract approval backlog described above.

CONCLUSION

BTOP and BIP, as established by the Recovery Act, are intended to promote the availability and use of broadband Internet access throughout the country, as well as create jobs and stimulate economic development. The ability to measure the progress of BTOP and BIP projects and their effects on expanding access to and use of broadband Internet access is an important component of program management and oversight, and could inform future federal programs. NTIA and RUS track the amount of funds disbursed to projects as one measure of progress. However, disbursements do not fully reflect the amount of progress made. Thus, data on non-financial measures of progress, such as the amount of infrastructure deployed, can provide insights into the progress of broadband projects. While NTIA established performance measures and collected data on non-financial measures of progress, RUS did not initially collect comparable data, and once it did begin collecting these data, it could not ensure their quality. Collecting accurate data would enable RUS to better demonstrate BIP projects' progress toward completion, and outcomes for the BIP program. We also identified challenges that NTIA and RUS both faced in ensuring the accuracy of projects' subscribership data. Because both agencies have taken steps to improve the quality of the subscribership data reported by awardees, we are not making a recommendation to address this issue in this report.

RECOMMENDATION FOR EXECUTIVE ACTION

To ensure RUS is collecting reliable information regarding the effect of investments in broadband, we recommend that the Secretary of Agriculture direct RUS to take steps to improve the quality of its data on the number of fiber miles and wireless access points created by BIP projects.

AGENCY COMMENTS AND OUR EVALUATION

We provided a draft of this report to the Secretary of Commerce and the Secretary of Agriculture for review and comment. The Department of Commerce provided technical comments that we incorporated into the report as appropriate. The Department of Agriculture provided written comments on a draft of this report. The department disagreed with our characterization that RUS does not collect adequate data to measure the progress of BIP and noted that RUS collects financial data as well as contract-level data with information on planned construction for each project. The department also noted that RUS collects data on the number of subscribers, which it implies is a relevant measure of performance for the BIP program. We agree that RUS collects financial data, but as we note in the report, financial data do not fully reflect the progress of the program. Thus, non-financial data, such as fiber miles and wireless access points deployed, provide an additional indicator of BIP's progress. As we note in the report, RUS's data for these measures, as well as the number of subscribers, are unreliable, which hinders RUS's ability to assess the progress of BIP. Although the department neither agreed or disagreed with our recommendation that RUS should improve the quality of its data on the number of fiber miles and wireless access points created by BIP projects, the department stated that RUS has already taken steps to improve the quality of its data. If RUS takes action and can demonstrate that the data are reliable, we will close the recommendation as implemented.

Mark L. Goldstein
Director, Physical Infrastructure

APPENDIX I. SCOPE AND METHODOLOGY

This appendix provides information on the methodologies that we used to assess (1) the progress made in implementing broadband projects funded by the American Recovery and Reinvestment Act of 2009 (Recovery Act),[20] (2) the effect of the projects on expanding access to and adoption of broadband service, and (3) the challenges that grant and loan recipients face in completing broadband projects, and the actions that agencies are taking to help address these challenges.

Progress of Programs

To determine the progress made in implementing the projects funded by the Recovery Act, we obtained data that allowed us to calculate the amount of funds awarded and the amount of funds disbursed to projects participating in the Broadband Technology Opportunities Program (BTOP) administered by the National Telecommunications and Information Administration (NTIA), and the Broadband Initiatives Program (BIP) administered by the Rural Utilities Service (RUS). In addition, we obtained data from NTIA on the status of BTOP in meeting the targets for the key performance indicators established by NTIA: miles deployed or leased, community anchor institutions connected, workstations installed in public computer centers, and new broadband subscribers. To determine the reliability of these data, we reviewed relevant documentation, including manuals, guidance and forms provided to awardees reporting the data, descriptions of internal controls, and Inspector General reviews of the data from the Department of Agriculture and the Department of the Treasury (which manages the payment system used by BTOP recipients); and we interviewed agency officials about their processes for reviewing the data and ensuring their accuracy. We found the data generally reliable for our purposes of reporting the amount of funds disbursed to BTOP and BIP awardees, and the amount of progress made toward meeting NTIA's targets for BTOP, although we did note and report on limitations with NTIA's subscribership data.

Effect of Programs

To assess the effect of the projects on expanding access to and adoption of broadband service, we reviewed data collected by NTIA and RUS, such as the aforementioned data on the progress of BTOP projects in deploying miles, connecting community anchor institutions, installing workstations in public computer centers, and creating new broadband subscribers. Our efforts to determine the reliability of BTOP's program data are discussed above. We reviewed the data that RUS collects from BIP awardees on the number of subscribers accessing BIP-funded service, but based on conversations with RUS officials, determined the data were not reliable for our purposes. We also interviewed BTOP and BIP awardees to understand the effects of their individual projects. We used the following criteria to select awardees to interview: projects that had received two-thirds of their award (thereby meeting NTIA's "substantially complete" requirement), large award size, and geographic dispersion.

Challenges

To determine the challenges that grant and loan recipients face in completing projects, we interviewed NTIA and RUS officials, including NTIA's Federal Program Officers (FPO) and RUS's General Field Representatives (GFR), who serve as a point-of-contact for the awardees. We also interviewed the BTOP and BIP awardees mentioned in the previous paragraph, as well as some awardees that had not received two-thirds of their award. For BTOP, we reviewed awardees' progress reports for the first quarter of 2012,[21] which covered the time period from January 1, 2012, to March 31, 2012. In these quarterly reports, awardees must report on their progress toward meeting milestones (progress is based on expenditures), and describe the reason for any variance from their baseline plan or subsequent written updates provided to their program officer. Awardees must also describe any challenges or issues faced in the past quarter in achieving planned progress, and any areas where assistance from NTIA is needed. We created content categories for the challenges reported by the awardees and for whether they requested assistance from NTIA. Two analysts independently coded each response into one of the categories; any discrepancies in the coding of the two analysts were discussed and addressed by the analysts. For BIP, we reviewed a tracking spreadsheet maintained by RUS, in which the GFRs provide the status of each BIP project and in some cases, note issues or challenges facing individual projects.

Agency Actions to Address Challenges

To determine the actions NTIA and RUS are taking to address challenges facing BTOP and BIP awardees, we interviewed NTIA and RUS officials, including FPOs and GFRs. We also reviewed documentation of guidance, training, webinars, and workshops provided by the agencies. We asked the BTOP and BIP awardees we interviewed about their experiences with NTIA and RUS, including whether the awardees had faced challenges and the awardees' perceptions of NTIA and RUS guidance and resources.

We conducted this performance audit from November 2011 through September 2012 in accordance with generally accepted government auditing standards. Those standards require that we plan and perform the audit to obtain sufficient, appropriate evidence to provide a reasonable basis for our findings and conclusions based on our audit objectives. We believe that the evidence obtained provides a reasonable basis for our findings and conclusions based on our audit objectives.

APPENDIX II. ANALYSIS OF EMPLOYMENT DATA SUBMITTED BY PROGRAM AWARDEES

This appendix responds to a recurring GAO mandate in the American Recovery and Reinvestment Act (Recovery Act) requiring us to comment and report quarterly on estimates of jobs funded and counted as full-time equivalents (FTE) as reported by recipients of Recovery Act funds.[22] To assess the quality of FTE reporting by awardees participating in the National Telecommunications and Information Administration's (NTIA) Broadband Technology Opportunities Program (BTOP) and the Rural Utilities Service's (RUS) Broadband Initiatives Program (BIP), we examined recipient-reported data publicly available at Recovery.gov as of August 1, 2012, for these two programs over the 10 quarters in which they reported FTE data.[23] While Recovery Act recipients' reporting of FTEs began in September 2009, the first quarter that FTE data were submitted for the BTOP and BIP programs was the first quarter of 2010 for BTOP and the second quarter of 2010 for BIP.

Our assessment of the FTE reporting included interviewing NTIA and RUS program officials familiar with awardees' recipient reporting and a review of the FTE figures and other recipient reported data. Our matches showed a high degree of agreement between the agencies' assessments of FTE positions reported and our analyses of information recipients provided on their quarterly reports. Based on our analyses and interviews with agency officials, we determined that the recipient-reported data appeared to be sufficiently reliable for the purpose of providing summary, descriptive information about FTEs and other information submitted on grantees' recipient reports.[24]

The FTE data reported by BTOP and BIP recipients showed an overall rise in the level of employment activity among the projects. As shown in figure 3, the number of FTEs reported by both programs steadily increased from quarter to quarter in 2010 and 2011 with BTOP continuing to show an increase in the second quarter of 2012 while BIP showed a decrease during the first quarter of 2012, and an increase from that in the second quarter of 2012.

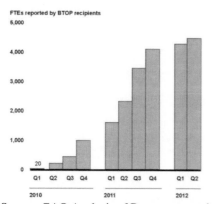 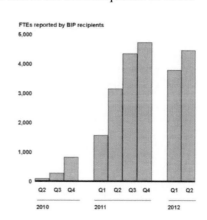

Source: GAO Analysis of Recovery.gov data.

Notes: FTE values are shown for each individual quarter and are not cumulative. Technical assistance awards for BIP are not included in the totals.

Figure 3. FTEs Reported by BTOP and BIP Recipients, January 2010 through June 2012.

Recipients reported that BTOP-funded FTEs increased from about 20 FTEs in the first quarter of 2010 to a peak quarter of about 4,500 FTEs in the second quarter of 2012. BIP recipients reported an increase from 86 FTEs in the second quarter of 2010 to about 4,500 in the second quarter of 2012, with a peak of over 4,700 FTEs in the fourth quarter of 2011.

End Notes

[1] The term broadband commonly refers to high speed Internet access. GAO, *Telecommunications: Broadband Deployment Is Extensive throughout the United States, but It Is Difficult to Assess the Extent of Deployment Gaps in Rural Areas*, GAO-06-426 (Washington, D.C.: May 5, 2006).

[2] Pub. L. No. 111-5, 123 Stat. 115 (2009).

[3] Of the $4.7 billion provided to NTIA, approximately $293 million was used to fund 56 grants to states and territories for the purposes of gathering broadband data in order to develop and maintain a nationwide map on the availability of broadband service, with some funds to be transferred to the Federal Communications Commission for the development of the national broadband plan. These activities are not included in our review. Recovery Act, 123 Stat., 128 and div. A, title VI, 123 Stat., 512, codified at 47 U.S.C. § 1305.

[4] Recovery Act, div. A, title I, 123 Stat., 118-119.

[5] Several factors contribute to the discrepancy between the funds appropriated for BTOP and the funds awarded. On August 10, 2010, Congress rescinded $302 million from BTOP, reducing the program's funding to approximately $4.4 billion. See Pub. L. No. 111-226, § 302, 124 Stat. 2389, 2404. NTIA also terminated one award, had one awardee not accept an award, and four awardees terminate their project voluntarily.

[6] The amount of funds awarded by RUS exceeds its appropriation because RUS can award and obligate funds in excess of its budget authority through the use of loans. For grants, the face amount of each grant is charged against RUS budget authority. However, the Federal Credit Reform Act of 1990, Pub. L. No. 101-508, div. A, title XIII, § 13201(a), 104 Stat. 1388-609, codified at 2 U.S.C. ch. 17A, subch. III, requires RUS to account for the budgetary impact of loans by estimating the expected net loss (or gain) of loans. This net amount, which is estimated by calculating the net present value of all cash flows to and from RUS over the lifetime of the loans, is referred to as the subsidy cost of the loans. RUS must charge the subsidy cost of loans to its budget authority. In addition, as of June 2012, RUS had terminated 38 BIP awards.

[7] GAO, *Recovery Act: Broadband Program Awards and Risks to Oversight*, GAO-11-371T (Washington, D.C.: Feb. 10, 2011); *Recovery Act: Further Opportunities Exist to Strengthen Oversight of Broadband Stimulus Programs*, GAO-10-823 (Washington, D.C.: Aug. 4, 2010); and *Recovery Act: Agencies Are Addressing Broadband Program Challenges, but Actions Are Needed to Improve Implementation*, GAO-10-80 (Washington, D.C.: Nov. 16, 2009).

[8] Recovery Act, div. A, title IX, § 901, 123 Stat.,191. Updates on GAO's oversight of Recovery Act funds can be found at: http://gao.gov/recovery. As of July 20, 2012, the Department of the Treasury had paid out $255.2 billion in Recovery Act funds for use in states and localities.

[9] Recovery Act, div. A, title XV, § 1512(e), 123 Stat., 287. FTE data provide insight into the use and impact of the Recovery Act funds, but recipient reports cover only direct jobs funded by the Recovery Act. These reports do not include the employment impact on suppliers (indirect jobs) or on the local community (induced jobs). Both data reported by recipients

and other macroeconomic data and methods are necessary to understand the overall employment effects of the Recovery Act.

[10] 74 Fed. Reg. 33104, 33110 (2009).

[11] Pub. L. No. 111-5, § 1512(e), 123 Stat. 115, 288. FTE data provide insight into the use and impact of the Recovery Act funds, but recipient reports cover only direct jobs funded by the Recovery Act. These reports do not include the employment impact on suppliers (indirect jobs) or on the local community (induced jobs). Both data reported by recipients and other macroeconomic data and methods are necessary to understand the overall employment effects of the Recovery Act. OMB defines FTEs as the total number of hours worked and funded by Recovery Act dollars within the reporting quarter divided by the quarterly hours in a full-time schedule. OMB Memorandum, M-10-08, *Updated Guidance on the American Recovery and Reinvestment Act – Data Quality, Non-Reporting Recipients, and Reporting of Job Estimates* (Dec. 18, 2009).

[12] NTIA adjusted the projected benefits estimated in BTOP recipients' initial applications. NTIA revised projections to reflect changes in the projects that occurred after awards were made, such as rerouting of planned broadband networks because of environmental issues or changes in partners. Total miles were reduced from 127,072 to 75,000, community anchor institutions connected were reduced from 29,557 to 15,000, new workstations were reduced from 35,334 to 35,000, and subscribers were reduced from 785,862 to 500,000. NTIA officials told us they raised three of the projections to 110,000 miles, 18,000 community anchor institutions, and 37,500 workstations.

[13] RUS is collecting data on subscribers to show the effect of BIP on broadband adoption, which we discuss later in this report. However, we do not consider this a measure by which one can evaluate the progress of a project toward completion.

[14] Pub. L. No. 91-190, 83 Stat. 852 (1970), as amended, codified at 42 U.S.C. ch. 55.

[15] Pub. L. No. 89-665 (1966), as amended, codified at 16 U.S.C. ch. 1A, subch. II.

[16] As mentioned previously, BTOP awardees are required to submit reports on a quarterly basis that among other things, discuss projects' progress made during the preceding 3 months and discuss challenges as to why projects may not have met their targets. These reports only include the challenges awardees reported during this period. Awardees may have experienced these or other challenges in prior quarters.

[17] Recovery Act, div. A, title XVI, § 1606, 123 Stat. 303.

[18] We previously reported on the need for FCC to reform the Universal Service Fund. GAO, *Telecommunications: FCC Has Reformed the High-Cost Program, but Oversight and Management Could be Improved*, GAO-12-738 (Washington, D.C.: July 25, 2012).

[19] In the Matter of Connect America Fund, 26 FCC Rcd. 17663 (2011), as corrected, 27 FCC Rcd. 4040 (2012).

[20] Pub. L. No. 111-5, 123 Stat. 115 (2009).

[21] NTIA requires that BTOP awardees submit quarterly and annual progress reports.

[22] Pub. L. No. 111-5, § 1512(e), 123 Stat. 115, 288 (2009). FTE data provide insight into the use and impact of the Recovery Act funds, but recipient reports cover only direct jobs funded by the Recovery Act. These reports do not include the employment impact on suppliers (indirect jobs) or on the local community (induced jobs). Both data reported by recipients and other macroeconomic data and methods are necessary to understand the overall employment effects of the Recovery Act.

[23] In addition to conducting our analyses of recipient report data for BIP and BTOP programs under the Recovery Act, we continued, as in prior rounds, to perform edit checks and analyses on all prime recipient reports to assess data logic and consistency and identify unusual or atypical data.

[24] We did notice, however, in our review of BIP's FTE data that some recipients did not report their FTEs in accord with RUS guidance. Recipients that received awards that were a combination of loans and grants were to report FTEs separately for each component of the award. RUS officials stated that they instructed the recipients that funds should be drawn

down proportionally from the loan and grant, and to divide FTEs along that same proportion. Thus, if the award is 50 percent loan and 50 percent grant, then FTEs for the entire project were to be divided evenly between the grant and the loan reports for the reporting quarter. We observed that there were recipients who received combination awards with different, unequal grant and loan award amounts, but reported FTEs equally split between the loan quarterly report and the grant quarterly report. The apportioning of the FTEs did not match the apportioning of the loan and grant amounts. RUS officials stated that without following up with the individual recipients, they could not determine the reason for this.

INDEX

D

E

F

G

H

S

T